Darn Those Miserable Yangkhis … and other stories from the Viet Nam War

by Joseph M. Puggelli

Modus Operandi Books

Modus Operandi Books • New York

To Patricia Vaccarino, my wife and best friend, who helped me to Come Home

And to Hayden Brumbeloe, who I never met in person but who has been with me since the day we met in spirit

Published 2021 by Modus Operandi Books

ISBN: 978-1-7365462-0-8

Printed in the U.S.

TABLE OF CONTENTS

Darn Those Miserable Yangkhis

The Untold True Story of How the Dodgers Leaving Brooklyn Caused the Viet Nam War

Introduction

In the last part of my tour, as a result of a deal between my unit commander and the Chief of Station of the local C. I. A. District Office, I was detached from my army unit and assigned to the Agency's District Office in Bien Hoa City, the capitol of Bien Hoa Province.

My army unit was headquartered at Long Binh, which was not far from Bien Hoa City. I had spent very little time at Long Binh. From the second week of my tour I had been attached, on a permanent temporary duty status, to a sensor unit that operated in the Dong Ngai Secret Zone.

(A short digression: one, by this time in my military service I was accustomed to, and unfazed by, many things that would have fazed me before, including oxymorons; two, if you don't know what sensors were, or how they were used in Viet Nam, go to the beginning of Chapter 2 in Darn Yangkhis for an explanation, most of which is serious, especially the part about the Nixon and McCarthy sensors ☺.)

My unit commander at Long Binh, Lt. Col. Bob Slocum, was a drinking companion, poker-playing buddy, and skirt-chasing buddy of the C. I. A. Bien Hoa District Chief of Station. Slocum offered to help out the Chief, Marty Gerber, who was taking shit from his boss, the C. I. A.'s Bien Hoa Province Chief.

Vietnamese districts are roughly the equivalent of American counties, and provinces are akin to states. Marty's problem was that, unlike all of his fellow county Chiefs in Viet Nam, who were long distances from, and therefore to a certain extent isolated from, Agency Higher Ups, his county happened to be right next to the state capitol and the Governor.

So, unfortunately for Marty, his District Office was only a mile from the C. I. A.'s Province Headquarters, and the Chief of Province could, and did, regularly stop by to complain to Marty about Marty's unit's lack of intelligence productivity.

By this time in my tour, finding out that I had volunteered for something that I was ignorant of was nothing new to me. I had learned from several such situations that it's rare that this thing you volunteered for, that you had no memory of volunteering for, turns out to be fun; and it's even more rare when it turns out to be less dangerous than the job you were leaving.

So I was more than a little anxious when I returned from a sensor-planting operation and was informed that I had once again volunteered for a special assignment. But, since I had no choice in the matter, complaining was a waste of time; and the Universe had made abundantly clear to me that I needed a change of scenery.

The areas in which we were planting sensors were increasingly infested with booby traps, and on a recent mission while walking point I had hit a trip wire that was intended to explode an 81 millimeter mortar round that was wired to a bush that was less than a foot from me. The trigger mechanism fired, but the hammer caught on a branch just short of detonating the mortar round, fortunately both for Mrs. Puggelli's favorite son and for the man immediately behind me, who probably would have been hit by fragments of the mortar round and definitely would have been hit by fragments of me.

This was the second time I had tripped a booby trap and the second time that it didn't kill or mutilate me, and I knew that my luck account was overdrawn and would not support a third check.

So even though I had no clue why the C. I. A. had drafted me, and had no clue about what I was going to do, a condition which reminded me of being drafted the first time, I jumped at the move, hoping that when you leap from the frying pan you don't always land in the fire.

This second drafting led to one of the great learning experiences of my life. It also caused an immediate major and positive change in lifestyle.

I went from sleeping in the rain and mud to having my own room and bed, with maid service, in the walled and heavily guarded compound of an old French villa in Bien Hoa city, with a French-trained chef who created great meals for those of us who inhabited the villa; and I dressed in civilian clothes and didn't have to salute military officers on those rare times that I came into contact with them. In fact, on one occasion an Army Major saluted me.

In the evening I would go out and sit with our off-duty guards and their families and drink homemade rice wine, practice my Vietnamese, and listen to their stories of fighting the Japanese, the French, the Viet Cong, and occasionally each other; and the stories were true.

We were regularly joined by members of the local Provincial Recon Unit, a collection of likeable criminals, killers, rogues and miscreants who were ethnic Nungs, rather than Vietnamese, and whose stories were even more incredible than those of our Vietnamese guards; and their stories were also true.

Even better, my work turned out to be fascinating. My job was to debrief Chieu Hois at the Province Chieu Hoi center and then to write reports highlighting any intelligence I had gotten.

The Chieu Hoi program was an attempt by the South Vietnamese government to encourage defection from the VC.

Chieu Hoi Leaflets were dropped by airplane over enemy-controlled areas. Any VC could "chieu hoi" (the term loosely translates as "open arms") by presenting a leaflet to an American or South Vietnamese army unit. The Chieu Hoi would, in theory and often in fact, receive preferential treatment that included indoctrination at a Chieu Hoi center, as opposed to a prison camp, and eventually be assimilated back into society.

I was told from the beginning by the C. I. A. Deputy Chief of Station, a very nice guy named Dave Kounzilman, that it was unlikely that I would learn any useful intelligence during my debriefs/interrogations, given that by the time a Chieu Hoi got to the Province center, he (or the occasional she) had already been interrogated several times at lower levels, and so whatever they knew was, presumably, already in the Intelligence pipeline. And most of the Cheiu Hois were the VC equivalent of what I had been, a grunt with a rifle who did what he was told to do and was not a fount of valuable intelligence.

In the true spirit of the American experience in Viet Nam, Dave emphasized that it was very important that I produce a lot of reports, even if they didn't say much, as the Province Chief, the one who was giving Marty shit, was more concerned about the number of reports coming from the District office than he was about the quality of the reports.

Truth to tell, when I started going to the Province Chieu Hoi Center, I didn't care if I ever got any intelligence. I was just fascinated to be able to talk, via my interpreter, Dzung, to the men and women who were a Vietnamese version of me, men and women who could help me understand better the Vietnamese people and culture, the war itself, and, of course, myself.

My interpreter Dzung was, as were many citizens of
Bien Hoa City, a Catholic whose family had
relocated to South Viet Nam after the French defeat.
Whip smart, he was a treasure trove of interesting
and valuable information about Vietnamese culture;
and he had a talent for listening to a Chieu Hoi's
story and noticing little details that were
inconsistent.

Several times he pointed out Chieu Hois who were,
he was convinced, of a higher rank than they
admitted to; and he was always right. It was not
unknown, he told me, for VC facing imminent
capture or death to Chieu Hoi as the best option
available in a bad situation; and a higher ranking
VC, whether of military or political rank, would then
pretend to be a lowly grunt of no intelligence value,
or a simple farmer who had been drafted by those
dastardly Viet Cong, until he could he could safely
defect from his defection and go back to his unit or
village. These were known as "false ralliers."

Dzung and I worked well together and had some fun
in the process. He taught me to say in Vietnamese,
"Enough of these stupid questions. Let's just shoot
this son of a bitch and then go have a beer," and
when we had a Chieu Hoi who was trying to fly
under the radar screen, we would go into our "Bad
Cop (me) and Good Cop (Dzung) routine.

At a pre-arranged signal I would angrily get up and
leave the debriefing room. Dzung would give the
Chieu Hoi a coke and commiserate with him,
"Listen, this American is bat shit crazy, even by

American standards, and you know how crazy Americans are. Just the other day he took a Chieu Hoi out back and shot him. You have to give me something he can take to his boss so I can save you from this crazy fucking American."

Even the less dramatic debriefings were fascinating, at least to a country boy from upstate New York with an interest in understanding Life. The very first Cheiu Hoi I debriefed was a North Vietnamese kid who had run away from his village to avoid the draft. Turned in by his relatives (pause for a second, think about that, and ask yourself what the hell we were doing fighting a people like that on their own turf), he was drafted, sent South and ended up with a VC main force unit.

I talked to him for eight hours. I had him walk me through his life in North Viet Nam, his trip down the Ho Chi Minh Trail, and his experiences in joining a VC unit, where the cultural differences between the northerners and the southerners made his assimilation more difficult than an American would expect, given that they were all Vietnamese who were glorious soldiers of Uncle Ho.

By this time in the war, many supposedly Southern VC were North Vietnamese soldiers who had been sent south to augment decimated VC units; and Northern and Southern Vietnamese have many of the differences that characterize northern and southern Americans, including, depending on your perspective, a funny way of talking and an excessively anal, or an excessively laid back, way of looking at the world.

I wrote up the interview, expecting nothing from a report which I found interesting but which, I assumed, the Rest of the World would find boring (as is usually the case with things I find interesting). In it I included details about daily village life in North Viet Nam and I described what he'd told me about manpower shortages in his village and district caused by the ever more frequent military drafts and about the gangs of sex-starved North Vietnamese women who were kidnaping and raping the few mostly young or old men who were available in his village, the rest having been drafted into the North Vietnamese army.

As ordered, I sent the report to the CIA Province headquarters. Several days later I was called into Marty's office. He told me that the Province Chief had called him to congratulate him on "that fine report your new debriefer wrote," which "ended up in Nixon's presidential daily brief."

After this lucky break I was golden, and nobody in the Army or the Agency would fuck with me. It turned out that the stuff I wrote about, which was really more cultural than military, was news to the Powers That Be, who ate it up and called for more.

I did note to myself that, given that it was 1969 and the war had been going on for a long time, it was disconcerting that the details I described were newsworthy to the Powers That Be who, you would think, would have known these things before they decided to go fight a war with people who defined the words "tough," "stubborn," and "committed." I bet there were not many American draft dodgers who were turned in by their relatives.

Some nights I'd take a jeep (and an M-16; Bien Hoa was relatively safe at night, but the key word in that phrase is "relatively") and drive to the C. I. A. Province headquarters for the nightly movie, snacks, and drinks. There I met and hit it off with John Prine, the man who read my reports and who then sent them on to his boss, the Province Chief.

John turned out to be a former Brooklynite who shared my skewed sense of humor, my passion for the Brooklyn Dodgers, and my dislike of all things Los Angeles, that thieving city that had stolen our beloved Dodgers, and in which he had spent his high school years before going on to Princeton.

Irreverence has always been one of my many character flaws, and I got into the habit of interspersing my actual reports with what I thought were funny faux reports. These stretched the boundary between the extreme reality that is always lurking around the corner in a combat zone and the absurdity that is on any given day one short step over the border of extreme reality. I knew that John would chuckle over the faux reports, put them in the burn-trash bin, and send the real ones on.

And so, in between serious reports there were born the stories of the PIZZA missile, the So Bo theorem, and the Met Offensive. Years later, after I had returned home and had, I thought, put all that nonsense behind me, one day, much to my surprise, Darn Yangkhis began to emerge.

Now, as a much older man, I think that Darn Yangkis is no more unreal or absurd than many of the things that I saw, did, and had done to me as a soldier in Viet Nam; or as a veteran of that war coming home to a culture that blamed us for doing our duty, a duty that Our Country had once deemed necessary and important, before they changed their mind.

**Part I, wherein the reader meets
several important characters
and is given some insight into
our Hero's eventual failure.**

Chapter 1
The Genesis of the Problem

"I know you two guys just got back from a long, tough patrol, but we got a big problem. Something bad—very bad—has happened out at Camp Breast. We think the VC overran it last night, and there's a good possibility that they used some sort of new weapon."

The speaker was Captain Cohen. The speakees were me and Sgt. Nguyen Trung, my friend, fellow soldier, and partner in crime, rice wine consumption, and other assorted peccadilloes, including the unauthorized pursuit of bar girls in off-limits bars, not to mention the authorized pursuit of bar girls in on-limits bars.

"Sir," I said, "we just returned from sixteen hard days in the Miasmic Swamp of No Return. Personally, I don't care if the VC dropped a neutron bomb on Breast. It's not our problem. We need some rice wine, sleep, food, and more rice wine before we have to go out again."

"Dai uy," said Trung, cutting as usual to the heart of the matter, "tai sao chumg toi khomg biet? Phup dhuop dau Le Tiet Bhig chuc chuoc." (Captain, why don't you just get to the bottom line? Tell us what you know happened at The Big Tit ((the Vietnamese translation of Camp Breast)) and what you think happened.)

Cohen, who was fluent in Vietnamese, like all
Americans in the elite, Top Secret Zebra Force,
said, "Bang bong bing bhuoung xinh phie cu hoi bop
buop. Duop phai tien lau do phap phlap." (We
know from radio reports that Breast got hit at 3:30
last night. They were reporting sappers in the wire
and incoming rounds when we lost all radio contact
for an hour. Communications since then have been
confusing at best and unintelligible at worst. We
can hear a horrible moaning and every once in a
while someone says, 'The Horror! O! The Horror!,
The Stink! O! The Smell!')

Trung, who spoke fluent English, like all Vietnamese
in the Zebra Force, said, "Why hasn't a relief force
gone in yet?"

Cohen responded, "Ai toi mot phuoc 'le Bhig'? Dau
tieng phang rang hau 'les Bhigs' nghia." (What the
hell do I look like, a fucking General? Higher
Headquarters probably didn't want to send anyone
into a disastrous situation that no one understands
yet.)

"What the hell else have we been doing during this
entire fercockta war?" I asked, adding, "Let me
guess why you're telling us all this: Trung and I
have been accorded the honor of having
volunteered to find out, at the possible price of life
and limb—our lives and our limbs, I might add —
exactly what happened Out There."

Cohen answered, "Tien Ti (my Zebra Force
nickname, which in Vietnamese means "The big

ugly one with the exceedingly funny nose who isn't as dumb as he looks, but, then again, who could possibly be that dumb?"), do you really think that I, knowing that you just returned from The Miasmic Swamp of No Return, would send you and Trung out again all by yourself? I'm hurt— no, don't interrupt—seriously, I'm hurt . . .. Actually, we're sending you two in with a company of the 201st Airborne."

"A company of the 201st Airborne?" I groaned. "Captain, you know what's going to happen. We'll get on the helicopters with those guys, and one of them will look at Trung and say something about the dumb gook, and I'll smash the idiot in the face with a rifle butt, or someone will look at me and say something about my nose, and Trung will smash him in the face with a rifle butt. You know we Zebra Forcers just don't get along with regular troops."

Cohen came back at me with his ultimate argument winner, "Gentlemen, let us remember that everyone in this unit, Vietnamese and American alike, is a volunteer. We all knew the risks, we all bought the ticket, and we all take the ride. You two are the best we have, and you're going in with the 201st. General Eastlessland asked General Siegal to send along two men who are so tough and so experienced, so nasty and so vicious, who smell so bad that they stand a chance, however small— or, perhaps, if the truth were to be told, even tiny—of getting out alive, no matter how bad things are at Breast. We can afford the loss of a company of the 201st, although God Knows how much Bad Press we'll get, but we have to find out what happened Out There."

"OK, OK," I grumbled. "You need tough, experienced, nasty, and vicious: that's why Trung's going. But what about me? I'm an avowedly chickenhearted and essentially worthless wimp who faints at the sight of blood, even when it's not my own."

Cohen chuckled, "I've got to hand it to you, Puggelli. No matter how bleak a situation looks, no matter how tough things get, you never lose your sense of humor."

So who was kidding?

My problem— actually, one of my many problems— was analogous to the dilemma of this Greek guy I read about in my "Heathen Literature" course at Mary the Very Muscular and Extremely Militant Virgin Regional Catholic High School in Poughkeepsie, New York. The gods gave him the gift of prophetic sight, and then they made sure that no one ever believed him when he foretold the future.

In my case, almost everyone believed me when I was bullshitting, but no one took me seriously when I was telling the truth. No matter what I did or said, my fellow Zebra Forcers persisted in their perception of me as a tough, fearless, "Damn the Booby-traps, Fie Upon the Ambushes, Full Speed Ahead" brainless maniac just like they were.

It didn't matter that I frequently quoted Montesquieu, "If soldiers were rational, they would all run from the horror of war." It didn't matter that I slept with my Teddy Bear, Horace, when we were in base camp (Mom had sent Horace from home.). Everybody just assumed I was exercising what Captain Cohen called my "combination of iconoclastic individuality and dry, self-deprecating wit."

Part of the confusion between my reality and the general perception of my reality was attributable to a confluence of circumstances: Whatever else could be said about me, I did at least look like a soldier. May Thi Lin, a bar girl of formidable beauty and even more formidable intellect, often said I was built like a water buffalo; and I was a decorated combat veteran who had been awarded a medal after the Lost Patrol in the Loon Foon Forest (I still think all these years later that this medal was the second most undeserved medal in the history of warfare; without question the single most undeserved medal in the annals of human conflict was the one I would get after the Battle of the Big Breasted Woman, but more about the latter later.).

"Hell, Tien Ti," Cohen said, slapping me on the shoulder, "don't worry. If you wind up in a body bag, I'll take good care of Horace."

I kept quiet, since the issue was no longer in doubt. If "Wild Sy" Siegal said we were going, we were going. No one messed with our Padrone, who was an excellent specific example of my Uncle Rocco's frequently quoted general truism, "There's not a pubic hair's worth of difference between a good Sicilian and a good Jew."   Wearily, Trung and I gathered up our gear and headed for the chopper pad.

Chapter 2
A Pause in the Thread of Our Narrative to Describe How our Hero Joined the Zebra Force

I'm sure you're wondering how I, of all people, ended up in the Zebra Force.

Well, it wasn't planned and it wasn't easy, but there was a kind of weird logic to the whole thing.

First, I was drafted. Then, after Basic Combat Training and AIT (Advanced Infantry Training) at Fort Geshtalt in New Jersey, I was sent to the Defense Language Institute at Fort Philosophic Bliss, in Dog Dropping, Texas, for a Vietnamese language course. After graduation, I was assigned to Fort Unbearable Angst, in Arizona, where I was trained as a specialist in sensor employment and monitoring.

Sensors, first used extensively in Viet Nam, came in a variety of shapes and sizes and were programmed to detect, depending upon the particular sensing device in use, ground vibration caused by the movement of enemy equipment or troops, their body heat, or the metal of their weapons, or their farts. After sensors were dropped or planted in enemy territory, each device broadcast a signal that appeared as a number on a receiving screen. So, for example, if "27" appeared, the operator checked his target sheet on which the location of each sensor was plotted, verified the coordinates, and called an air or artillery strike on the area around sensor 27.

By this time (June, 1968) sensors had been used in Viet Nam for a while. However, I had been trained in the use of a whole new generation of sensors, including the Ultra-Top-Top Secret "Nixon" and "McCarthy" sensors.

The "Nixon" was a voice-activated device that would pick up all conversation within 30 meters and relay it back to a special Ultra Top Secret receiver. The "McCarthy" represented the cutting edge of anti-guerrilla technology. Each contained a computer that had been programmed to pick up any Marxist-Leninist-Maoist-Thoreauist thought patterns within a 100-meter area (One of the McCarthy's creators was unusually well read and saw immediately that Thoreau's emphasis upon the importance of following one's dreams and living by one's convictions was deeply suspicious at best and probably communist). Such patterns were also relayed to a special receiver.

When I got to Viet Nam, I was assigned to the 201st Airborne Division, the famous "Screaming Hummingbirds," and sent to the Division base camp at Phu Bhu for a week of administrative processing and general orientation.

We had some time off in the evenings, and I began doing three of my favorite things: drinking, practicing a new language, and establishing meaningful interpersonal relations with the indigenous women.

I was a pretty good linguist. Besides English, I spoke Italian, Russian, French, Sicilian, and a little-known Southern Sicilian dialect called Bonzoni Sicilian, which is named after the area (Bonzoni) in which both it and my ancestors originated. (These language skills resulted from my close relationship with my favorite uncle, Rocco, an eclectic man-of-the-world whose appearance belied his handful of street names, which included "the really nasty fink" and "the amazingly unwholesome rat bastard.").

Bonzoni Sicilian (B.S.) is a major deviation from the Indo-European linguistic norm. Unlike standard Sicilian, B.S. is a tonal language. The meaning or meanings of a given word depend upon a subtle emphasis given to the syllables of the word by the speaker.

Linguists who specialize in B.S. (all of them family, of course) have identified 12,767 separate tones in the language. There is only one vocabulary word, "Mafia."

Thus, for example, "Mafia" (pronounced MaFIYa) means "If you continue to act in that appallingly obnoxious fashion, thus disregarding my innate dignity and trampling upon the deeply sensitive being within me, I will smash your fucking face in"; yet "Mafia" (pronounced MAfiA) means "Man, can you believe the tits on that one!"

So one night I found myself in an off-limits Vietnamese bar in Phu Bhu, drinking Phu Bhu

Bhombs (a shot of beer in a glass of rice whiskey) and talking to a new friend, May Thi Lin.

In the bar—where, by the way, the few Americans present all spoke Vietnamese—I had noticed something interesting.

The spoken Vietnamese I was hearing sounded different from what I had learned at Ft. Philosophic Bliss. At the same time, it was strangely familiar. What's more, I kept hearing things that no other Vietnamese-speaking American seemed to hear.

Then came the incident that both explained the situation and changed my life forever.

Somebody tripped and fell against a patron, who dropped his rice wine into my lap. Startled, I began to curse—but in B.S., not Vietnamese.

Suddenly a Vietnamese man runs up to me. Instinctively I reach for my M-16, in case he is going to tell me how much he loves Democracy, hand me a hand grenade with the pin out, or describe to me in nauseating detail his sincere hatred of the Viet Cong.

Startled by my action, he jumps back, in case I'm going to pat him on the head and tell him how much I love the Vietnamese, call an air strike in on him and his village, or lecture him in nauseating detail about the virtues of Democracy. We both stand, tense and unsure of what to do next. I, who haven't been in Viet Nam long, am embarrassed by my paranoid reaction to his innocent action, which was, of course, stupid, since my reaction had only been proper, as, indeed, had been his response to my reaction to his action.

Nervous and frustrated, I spit out a common B.S. exclamation, 'Mafia!' (May you develop huge, ugly warts on your nose, and when you go to a doctor for help, may that doctor be a staggeringly beautiful woman with big bazooms who is as queer as a four-dollar bill.)

In the stunned silence that has enveloped the bar, the Vietnamese comes cautiously closer to me and says, 'Ma Phia Ia?', which I recognize, somehow, as "Is it really possible that there exists an ugly round-eye who understands even a little bit of what the hell we've been trying to say to you idiots ever since Dien Bien Phu fell?"

Of course, you can predict the rest: "Mafia?", I ask in shock. "Ma Phia Ia!!!", he replies with growing certainty. "Mafia Mafia?", I ask. He says, "Ma Phia Ia. Xien - Tho, Tien - La. Toi Noi Ma Phia Ia. Chung - Toi Noi Ma Phia Ia." "Mafia!", I gasp.

There it was. Don't ask me how or why, but Vietnamese and Sicilian B.S. were brother (or sister) languages.

Several days later my new Vietnamese friend, Sgt. Nguyen Trung, invited me to a party. Unbeknownst to me, Sgt. Trung was a member of the Ultra-Top-Sooper-Dooper-Secret Zebra Force.

As I was to learn later, most of the Vietnamese and all of other Americans at this party were also members of the Zebra Force. We were drinking Satchel Charges[1] (four shots of rice whiskey dropped into a canteen cup of beer), and I became slightly intoxicated. When under the influence, my command of any language, be it English, Vietnamese, or B.S., is not strong.

By the end of the evening, good fellowship and Satchel Charges flowed in equal measure. During one of my many trips to the bathroom, the Zebra Force members had caucused and decided that my garrulous nature, mastery of B.S., and gargantuan appetite for food and drink made me an ideal candidate for their elite unit.

There was, of course, the problem of my lack of combat experience, but the consensus was that my experiences as a boy growing up on the streets of Brooklyn would serve as an acceptable substitute. (I had, in truth, exaggerated just a bit my role in the Battle of Ralph Avenue and Avenue J, but I blame all that on the Satchel Charges.)

It was Sgt. Trung who asked me the formal question, "Dien lo quang xa Viet Cong phien do mo?", which means "Do you wish to become a member of our select band of brothers, who laugh in the face of death, who go in the way of danger, and

---

[1] A drink named after the lethal satchel charge used by NVA and VC assault units, a large block of explosive carried in a canvas satchel.

who deem it an honor to meet the Viet Cong in combat, preferably hand-to-hand, on their own turf?"

Inebriated as I was, I understood what I was being asked. My immediate reply was, "Phuong te tien phuoc lo? Viet Cong giet ngui my. Toi muon dien co Vietnamese. Toi khomg 'Zebra Force' anh lo 10,000."

Vietnamese, of course, is a tonal language. Each word has a variety of meanings depending upon the tone that the speaker gives it. A subtle change of tone creates an entirely different meaning. I thought I was saying, "What'reyoupeopleabsofuckiniglutely nuts? Those Viet Cong kill people, and they're not real big on Americans. I intend to spend the war pacifying Vietnamese bar maids. With all due respect, I wouldn't join the 'Zebra Force' in 10,000 years."

In fact, I was actually saying, "How can you even ask such a foolish question? I cherish the idea of playing footsie with the hated enemy, those deplorable egg-sucking Viet Cong, who trifle with the affections of young Vietnamese women. To become a member of the Zebra Force would be the greatest honor of my life, one that I could not hope to match even if I lived for 10,000 years."

The next day I was assigned to the Zebra Force. To tell you the truth, I had such a horrible hangover, I didn't care. Those damn Satchel Charges will kill you.

<u>Yet another pause in our Narrative, this time for
notes from our Editor</u>:

(1) Most American soldiers were at least mildly
disrespectful of their South Vietnamese allies, but
our Hero has nothing but good things to say about
Sgt. Nguyen Trung.

During Operation Futile Endeavor, Trung and
Puggelli spent a month in enemy territory on the top
of Nui Nui Nui Nu? (the site of the future Battle of
the Big Breasted Woman, which Puggelli describes
later and in which he and Trung played key roles).
During this time the two became unusually close,
even for Zebra Forcers.

Several factors contributed to this development:
each was fluent in two of the other's languages;
each was obsessed both with the size of Raquel
Welch's breasts and with the question of the
Meaning of Life (Trung maintained that the answer
to the latter was to be found in the dimensions of the
former); and both were hard-eyed cynics/hopeless
romantics (or hopeless romantics/hard-eyed cynics,
I mean, Come On, Who the hell can really tell the
difference?) who consumed huge quantities of
home-made rice wine regularly during off-duty hours
and occasionally during on-duty hours.

(2) Created after the Tet Offensive of 1968, the
Zebra Force was the brainchild of General Seymour
"Wild Sy" Siegal and was designed to act as an
intelligence-gathering infantry unit that would range
far into the hinterlands of Viet Nam and give the

allies ample warning if the enemy planned on launching another hammer blow like Tet '68, a major offensive that took the enemy months to prepare but which, incredible as it still seems today, caught the Americans and South Vietnamese by surprise, a surprise that had translated into that worst of all American military or political situations, Bad Press.

The Zebra, an animal whose coloration is created by an equal number of contrasting black and white stripes, was chosen as the symbol of this new unit because the Zebra Force would be equally composed of American and Vietnamese personnel, all of whom, by the way, had to be volunteers.

Siegal, a maverick officer who owed his stars, Washington insiders whispered, to the influence of the "bagel Mafia" in Congress, wanted all of the personnel in the Zebra Force to be soldiers with considerable experience fighting the VC, or their own military police, or, preferably, both. Moreover, he insisted that the American candidates for the Zebra Force had to be fluent in Vietnamese and the Vietnamese fluent in English.

By this time in the war, neither the idea of Long Range Reconnaissance Patrols nor the idea of real cooperation between the American military and the South Vietnamese military was new. The former had, with a few exceptions, not been properly implemented, and the latter was almost a pure fiction.

The average American soldier had little respect for— or understanding of—his South Vietnamese counterpart, and the South Vietnamese soldier was equally ignorant of and unenthusiastic about his self-proclaimed saviors.

Both sides gave much lip service to cooperation; yet, despite the obvious military and political advantages that would accrue if this cooperation were made real, the South Vietnamese and the Americans, from generals to privates, regarded each other with suspicion and hostility. "It was a hell of a way to fight a war," said the now retired General Siegal in a 1986 interview, "but then again, it was a hell of a war."

Siegal intended the Zebra Force to be an organization where, as he put it, "We keep bullshit to a minimum and we get rid of the assholes. The rest will work itself out."

For a number of reasons—not the least of which was the fear of what might happen if there were real cooperation between the two allies—both the American and South Vietnamese High Commands decided to give the Zebra Force a "Sooper Dooper Top Secret" classification. No official mention of the unit's existence ever appeared, and even today the records of the men who served in the Zebra Force are classified. "Wild Sy" Siegal was given a free hand to recruit for the Zebra Force, and he reported only to the commander of all American forces in Viet Nam, General William B. Eastlessland.

As is often the case with an unorthodox organization, the Zebra Force assumed the personality of its earthy, results-oriented commander.

In settled areas, the Zebra Force units generally followed traditional military behavior patterns. However, since Zebra Force members defined "settled area" as "somewhere where we ain't," it is probably fortunate that they were rarely in the proximity of regular military units or city-dwelling civilians.

Because so few officers, either Vietnamese or American, could serve effectively with (read: be accepted by) such soldiers, the Zebra Force units often went into the field without officer supervision. In such cases, these small, squad-sized units operated under the command of the best soldier in the group, a designation that was made by general acclaim.

Unorthodox though this system might have been, it was also effective.   The Zebra Force facilitated the development of outstanding leaders like the man who became Puggelli's best friend, Sgt. Nguyen Trung, who turned out to be a man of such exceptional common sense, wisdom, and courage that American Zebra Force members were known to attempt bribery to gain entrance to Trung-led patrols.

Of course, even though the existence of the Zebra Force was officially denied by the Powers That Be, word of the organization's existence spread throughout the military's grapevine. American and South Vietnamese traditionalists were opposed to the creation of "special" units like the Zebra Force because the soldiers in them didn't all dress the same but they all did know how to salute improperly. Progressives pointed out that much the same could have been said of George Washington's army, and at least we won that one.

As a result of this often bitter backroom infighting, the Joint Chiefs of Staff, in October 1969, asked the famous Israeli General Lev "Wild Lev" Ben Lev to go to Viet Nam and evaluate the Zebra Force. In a TOP REALLY SOOPER DOOPER SECRET report, Ben Lev, who had been a loud and persistent critic of U.S. strategy and tactics in Viet Nam, lauded the Zebra Force units as "tightly bonded bands of competent soldiers who rely more upon their experience and common sense than on technology." Added Ben Lev, "plus they drink a lot, and show me a soldier with a brain who doesn't drink a lot. I mean, what the fuck do you expect? You're out there trying to kill people who are trying to kill you. Man, that just is not natural, or at least it shouldn't be."

After the war the Communists themselves confirmed Ben Lev's estimate of the quality of the Zebra Force. In 1977, Vo Cua Mua, who during the war had been the National Liberation Front's Commissar in Charge of Unusual Sneakiness and Truly Dirty Tricks, said, "Except for using their technology and firepower in certain situations, the Americans never did anything that really bothered us.

"That is, except for that unusually sneaky and excessively dirty trick which those egg-sucking imperialist running-dogs called the Phoenix program (a highly effective program whereby CIA-led mercenaries targeted and killed villagers suspected of being Viet Cong, eliminating in the process many key members of the Viet Cong infrastructure and many Completely Innocent Individuals against whom Someone Had a Personal Grudge); and except, of course, for those 'phien cuas' (unreservedly bad no-goodniks who would steal rice seedlings from blind little old ladies) in the 'Lo muon phfiet' (a unit whose patch resembles a water buffalo that was attacked by a graffiti artist who had obviously imbibed too much rice wine)." ((Editor's note: a crude Vietnamese translation of Zebra Force)).

(3) . Puggelli's and Trung's commanding officer in the Zebra Force, Captain Moshe Giuseppe Cohen, was the Honor Graduate of the West Point class of 1965. At West Point Cohen was also an Honorable Mention All-American football player and the NCAA wrestling champion in the 167-pound weight class. Cohen's classmates voted him the odds-on favorite to be the first of their group to win a general's star.

After service in Germany and Korea, Cohen volunteered for Viet Nam. He compiled an outstanding record with the Zebra Force, and was then given command of a regular line company of the 201st. However, his experiences in Viet Nam, especially during the Battle of Phuocked Up Ridge, worked subtle changes in Cohen's attitude toward the military.

When he returned from Viet Nam, Cohen was stationed at Fort Benning, Georgia. At Benning, he rapidly developed a reputation for irreverence toward the Powers That Be. Ironically, the turning point of Cohen's military career, and perhaps of his life, occurred when he was being completely serious. At a presence-required party given by post commander General Hogan, Cohen, with what bystanders later described as absolute sincerity, told the General's wife that he had rarely seen a dog as beautiful as hers. Unfortunately, Mrs. Hogan was at the time showing Cohen a picture of her recently arrived grandson.

While serving in his new position as commander of the night guards at Fort Desolation in the Antarctic, Cohen decided that he would not make the military his career. He resigned his commission and went home to Long Beach, N.Y.

Experiencing a rootlessness characteristic of many combat veterans, Cohen pondered what to do with the rest of his life. He thought about becoming a lawyer but decided against it because, in his words, "I had already screwed up enough lives in Viet Nam."

Cohen began drinking heavily and had several mental breakdowns, including the three years he spent as a history teacher and offensive line coach at Woodmere Academy, an independent high school in Woodmere, Long Island.

In 1976, during a reunion/bacchanal (a tautology, some would say) of former Zebra Force members, Cohen met Puggelli's cousin, Angelina Epstein Fanucchi, who thought he was "cute, in a dorky kind of way."

The two were married six months later and, with the financial backing of Puggelli's Uncle Rocco, opened the first "Cohen's Cannoli Parlor." Two years later they franchised and became the first honest millionaires in the Family.

Chapter 3
The Narrative Resumes: Our Hero Gets Breast-ed

It was at Camp Breast that I learned the truth of another one of Uncle Rocco's oft-quoted maxims, this one being "No matter how bad It gets, shut up, because It could get worse, real fast."

"It," in this case, was my first awareness of the single enemy weapon that filled me with uncontrollable terror (as opposed to the controllable terror inspired by ambushes, booby traps, mortars, etc.): the "Personnel Impact ZZ-A" rocket, which we grunts came to call by its acronym, the "Pizza."

The Pizza missile looked almost exactly like the standard Soviet-made 122 millimeter rocket that the enemy had been using throughout the war.

The Pizza was the brainchild of North Vietnamese Commander-In-Chief General Vo Nguyen Giap, the ex-high school history teacher who had crushed the French at Dien Bien Phu.

Giap decided that the Communist forces needed a weapon that could be used against special American targets when the objective was not the destruction of American personnel or equipment, but rather their capture.

Giap's technicians created the Pizza by modifying the 122 millimeter rocket (the tail structure was changed to improve accuracy) and by removing the large explosive warhead and replacing it with a much smaller explosive charge and a new warhead composed of either 50 pounds of fermented anchovy pizza paste (the Pizza I, the "small pie") or of 75 pounds of fermented anchovy pizza paste (the Pizza II, the "large pie").

The theory behind the use of the Pizza was that the rockets would impact, explode, and cover the target area with great gobs of fermented anchovy pizza paste. Defenders would be rendered helpless by the disgusting, inhuman smell, and the Cong sapper squads, all equipped with sophisticated Soviet gasmasks, could safely carry out their assignments.

 Under conditions of great secrecy, the first Pizzas were sent south. In the worst of our many Intelligence failures of the Viet Nam War, the American High Command did not have an inkling of the presence of Pizzas in South Vietnam—until the VC overran Camp Breast, inflicting one of the worst defeats U.S. forces would suffer during the long, long war.

Later, when Trung and I were detached to the C.I.A. during Operation Manic Depression, I had the opportunity to interrogate the VC Commander, Captain Phung, who had led the daring assault on Breast. He had been captured a week after the assault on Breast.

As Phung described it, the VC attack on Breast was a classic combination of old tactics and new weapons.

At precisely 0330 hours, nine Pizzas came crashing down on one section of Camp Breast. As the rockets were exploding, four special five-man sapper squads were completing their journey through the minefields and barbed wire. At 0331 the rest of Breast was pounded by a barrage of 60 and 81 millimeter mortars. At 0332 the sapper squads penetrated the perimeter and headed for their objective.

Here, in the words of Phung himself, is what happened: "The plan was for our gunners to seal off an area of the Big Tit (the VC name for Camp Breast) just as we sappers got rid of the brassiere (penetrated the final rolls of barbed wire). Our gunners dropped four Pizzas in a rough line not far from the objective and five more Pizzas around the objective. The mortar fire on the rest of the Big Tit was designed to keep the Egg-Sucking Yang Khi Imperialists in their bunkers and out of our hair.

"We had been told what to expect, but none of us could believe how effective the Pizzas really were. Imperialist Dogs were vomiting all over the place. No one paid us any attention as we made our way to the mess hall and captured our objective, a copy of the film 'The Green Berets'."

I asked Phung what possible value the VC could see in the movie "The Green Berets" (a deathless flick which starred John Wayne as he mashed, mauled, and maimed thousands of extras impersonating Viet Cong guerillas, all in the name of Democracy and The American Way)?

"Our generals felt that we had a significant morale problem brewing, what with our troops forced to live in the jungle, often underground, and to fight the Armed Forces of the most powerful nation in the world, often without adequate medical supplies, and to go for months or years without sex. I'm telling you, being a jungle fighter isn't nearly as romantic as Jane Fonda makes it sound.

"So the plan was to capture a copy of 'The Green Berets' and to show it to the troops in our rest camps. The hope was that they would get a good laugh and morale would improve."

"Did the plan work?" I asked?

"Does a water buffalo shit in a rice paddy?" replied Phung. "'Have you seen that movie? I never laughed so hard in my life. John Wayne should have stuck to killing Indians and Japanese. We Viet Cong are out of his league.

"My favorite scene is where one of the Green Berets gets zapped by this huge bamboo trap that must have taken 10,000 man or woman hours to build. What self-respecting guerrilla fighter would waste time like that when he or she could spend 20 minutes wiring up and hiding a 105 millimeter shell and blow a whole squad of Yangkhis to dog meat?"

Intrigued as always by the enemy's ability to counter even our most sophisticated technology, I asked Phung how he and his men had been able to avoid the Nixon/McCarthy sensors, which had (in theory) protected Breast. His words illustrate the great adaptability which the uneducated enemy displayed in the face of the stuff Our Ivy League Guys came up with:

"Of course we knew that 'Hush-A-You-Mouth' and 'Hush-A-You-Mind' (the VC terms for Nixon and McCarthy sensors) receivers were on the Big Tit. We know when you guys are thinking about maybe getting ready to consider farting. But we don't think the 'Hush-A-You-Mouth' and the 'Hush-A-You-Mind' are quite as wonderful as you people do.

"The 'Hush-A-You-Mouth' does cause us a little trouble, especially if we don't know that they're in the area. But if we're moving through the jungle and come under artillery fire or an air strike for no good reason, we figure there are 'Hush-A-You-Mouths' somewhere close by and we tell our people to use different trails for a while. The 'Hush-A-You-Mouths' can't move. We can.

"The 'Hush-A-You-Mind' caused us real trouble the first time you used them, but once we figured out their weakness, it was a piece of noodle to guard ourselves against them.

"Now, when our men are moving through the jungle in an area where we think you Dog Breaths might have dropped some "Hush-A-You-Minds', we teach them to repeat to themselves certain slogans like 'John Foster Dulles was a Great American'; 'I love Jedgar Hoover'; or 'All evil in the world is caused by Communism, and anyone who doesn't agree is a Communist.'

"With enough of our people thinking such thoughts, we could march a whole division past a 'Hush-A-You-Mind' without setting it off.

Anyway, getting back to Breast, Trung, I and the relief company choppered into Breast early in the morning after the battle. We were all worried, because we didn't know what to expect. No one at headquarters knew exactly what had happened—all the communications from Breast were incoherent—but we could tell that something bad had happened.

It was worse than we thought.

Minus a frat party in college and several West 78th Street Association Christmas parties, I've never seen such a mess. And then there was that horrible, horrible stink....

The casualty list read as follows: VC, O WIA (Wounded In Action); O KIA (Killed In Action); U.S., O WIA; O KIA; 158 PIA (Pizza-ed In Action).

The 158 PIA's were in such bad physical and mental shape that they had to be flown to Japan and then to the states. No one of them ever returned to active duty.

If the guy in charge of the cover-up that followed the disaster at Breast had been in charge of covering up Watergate, Nixon would be a respected two-term President.

No mention of the defeat was ever made in the American press, and, outside of the immediate area, few people in Viet Nam heard anything more than rumors.

Later, when I had been ordered to volunteer for another assignment with the C.I.A., this time in support of Operation Bleak Outlook, I learned that the White House and the US. High Command were afraid that the enemy would attack with Pizzas on a massive scale. This would have meant the end of the war, unless we had countered with tactical nuclear weapons, as, apparently, some in the National Security Council were advising.

Fortunately, except for several other small-scale assaults where Pizza's were used (including the attack on at Binh Thinh, where the VC captured 12 cartons of new Playboys, and, of course, at the Battle of the Big Breasted Woman, which I will describe in detail later), the Cong never exploited the Pizza missiles the way they might have.

We later learned that the North Vietnamese Politburo had told Giap to shelve the Pizza, because the missile had caused a storm of controversy among top Communist leaders.

Giap had taken heavy political fire from two sources:
orthodox North Vietnamese ideologues objected to
the Pizza because it was unorthodox; also, many of
the older North Vietnamese thought the Pizza was,
as one of them phrased it to Giap during a rice-wine
break, "about as useless as tits on a water buffalo,"
because no one got blown to little bloody pieces
by it.

The US Army decided that, because of the threat of
Bad Press, the men who had been Pizza-ed at
Breast needed immediate and ongoing psychiatric
help (In the absence of the threat of Bad Press, of
course, the Army and the Government Could Give A
Shit Less about what happens to returning veterans.
Look what happened to the men and women with
Gulf War Syndrome, and those guys won.).

Major Minor, the officer in charge of the psychiatric
team assigned to work with the PIA's, kept in touch
with these unfortunates after they were discharged
and sent home. Minor conducted a comprehensive
interview of each member of the group on the 1st,
fifth, and tenth anniversaries of the Battle of Breast.
Because of my own severe Pizza-related post-
Vietnam mental problems (which, as you will come
to know, played a pivotal role in my ill-fated
romance with Donna La Madonna), I find the results
of this study very interesting:

Of the 158 PIA's, 12 were dead by 1979; 2 by Acts
of God (plane crash, car crash) and 10 by natural
causes (suicide, alcoholism, overdoses, cancer
caused by various completely safe toxic defoliants

used in Nam, etc.). The majority of the 146 surviving former PIA's showed unmistakable signs of continuing mental disorders: 22 had become high school teachers, 36 didn't cheat on their income tax, 94 were happily married, and—the most telling statistics of all—no one was seeing a psychiatrist or a psychologist on a regular basis (except for the three who had married psychiatrists and the five who had become psychologists), and no one had become a lawyer.

Part II, wherein the reader is first acquainted with some Surprising, possibly even Sensational, Stuff and then follows our Hero on a fateful patrol.

Chapter 1
Our Hero Begins to Understand
the War

I'm sure you will look askance at some of the
following, but I swear it's the Absolute Truth. Let me
begin in the middle:

Until about a month before the soon-to-be-described
disastrous patrol in the Loon Foon Forest, no
Vietnamese civilian or soldier, not even my close
friend Sgt. Trung, would speak to me directly about
the So-Bo Theorem. Later, after I saw the light, so
to speak, it hurt me more than a little bit that none of
my fellow soldiers, with whom I had hazarded life,
limb, and other essentials, and with whom I had
consumed enough rice wine to float the Titanic,
would open up to me.

But about this most sensitive of subjects, the
normally garrulous Vietnamese males were more
close-mouthed than Uncle Rocco's business
associates.

I remember with great clarity the night I learned
about So-Bo from my usual source of inside
information about Vietnamese culture, the bar girls,
with whom I spent as much time as I could, which
was never enough.

It was the evening of April 12, 1969. I was sitting
with May Thi Linh and Ti Ti Hue at my usual corner
table, located under the framed picture of Ebbets

Field that gave this out-of-the-way Vietnamese bar its curious name.

I was drinking Viet Cong Rockets (a double shot of moonshine rice whiskey in a bowl of homemade beer); the young ladies were making do with Booby Traps (a double shot of vodka in a glass of rice wine, with a twist).

Uncharacteristically, a palpable sense of gloom and depression filled Ebbets Field. Ti Ti Hue, who was of a more serious bent than the typical bar girl (On the night we met, Ti Ti Hue asked me, "What is your Weltanshauung?" "Gemini," I replied), was on the verge of tears, and even the irrepressible May Thi Linh was Deep in the Dumps. Each lady had downed three Booby Traps in my presence, and if the 14 empty bottles of Thirty-Three beer that formed a large "B" on the table in front of them told a true tale, my favorite bar maids had been imbibing for some time before I joined them.

I was more than a tad puzzled by the unusual ambience in Ebbets Field, since most of the regular employees and patrons - - a mix of Zebra Force members, local Self-Defense militia, and inhabitants of Phui Mui Village - - were de facto subscribers to Uncle Rocco's Philosophy of Life.

"Mike," my uncle had said to me on many occasions (Rocco called me 'Mike' even though my name is Joe. My uncle had once been the innocent victim of an FBI wiretap. Fortunately, the judge agreed with Rocco's contention that "Cut the Son of a Bitch into

12 pieces and put him—I mean 'them'— in the river"
could as easily be a reference to a badly made
lasagna as to the recently disappeared Frankie "The
Hairy Mustache" Persico.), "One must be mature
about life: Pain, suffering, death, and horror do not
constitute a good reason for having a bad time."

Depressed though they were, my lady friends had
downed enough booze to float an Armored
Personnel Carrier and were, consequently, a trifle
loose tongued. When I made yet another attempt to
lighten the mood of the moment by inquiring why a
bar in the boondocks of Viet Nam was named for
the home of my former favorite team, the verbal
floodgates opened, and I sat there in stunned
silence, as the two described in great detail the
cause of the Doom and Gloom that filled Ebbets
Field this night and the cause of the long-term
depression that had been visited first upon the
South Vietnamese people and then on those
American people dumb enough to let the Viet Nam
war affect them.

Both strands of Bad Karma were rooted in the So-
Bo Theorem.

According to May Lin and Ti Ti Hue, the So-Bo
Theorem was originated in 1959 or 1960 by a pair of
twins from Quang Tri, Mai Van So, a left handed
right fielder, and Mai Van Bo, a right handed left
fielder.

 These two stated in blunt language what was
simmering on the back burner of many a South

Vietnamese mind: that the National Front for The Liberation of South Vietnam, the Viet Cong, had originated as a spontaneous popular response to the Dodgers' leaving Brooklyn for Los Angeles.

 Mai Van So, who was the elder of the twins by five minutes, argued that the Viet Cong movement would be seriously hurt if either Duke Snider or Roy Campanella were appointed American ambassador to South Viet Nam, and would collapse completely if the Dodgers moved back to Brooklyn. Brother Bo, the younger and more radical of the two, thought that the departure of the Dodgers from Brooklyn was the definition of an Un-Doable Act, and that America, therefore, could never be trusted again.

 The split that had occurred between the two twins reflected the split that had taken place within the South Vietnamese population.

 When So told Bo that he was going to make contact with the CIA and seek to acquaint the American government with the So-Bo Theorem, Bo dropped a Chicom grenade into So's sleeping quarters. Bo then joined with other angry Vietnamese and created the National Front for the Liberation of South Vietnam and the Return of the Dodgers to Their One True Home, which our Intelligence analysts mistranslated into the Viet Cong.

May Lin cautioned me that, to the typical, fiercely proud, baseball-loving Vietnamese male, the So-Bo Theorem was so intertwined with the issues of masculine and national identity that it was unlikely that even a good friend like Sgt. Trung would speak openly to me, an American, about this subject.

So when I asked Trung about So-Bo, I was not surprised that he got up, walked agitatedly around the bunker, and then replied, "Tien-ti, toi khomg muon noi o cai nay la gi." (Even with a friend as dear as you, I cannot bring myself to speak openly about this matter.)

Fortunately, like the mind of God, with whom many Vietnamese and Sicilian men often confuse themselves, the Asian mind works in strange and mysterious ways. Sensing my sincere interest in this subject, and having been an eyewitness to the fact that I had paid enough dues to deserve to find out what this war was really all about, Trung maneuvered time, people, and circumstance so that I got a clear insight into the importance with which the Vietnamese regarded So-Bo.

Within two weeks of my question, Trung wangled an invitation for me and him to attend the birthday party for the commander of the ARVN 21st Division, in which his cousin was a captain.

There were about 20 men present—I was the only American—and it was a real feast: there were piles of shrimp, mounds of rice, platters of fish, skewers of dog, gallons of soup, rashers of rat, bowls of fish sauce, and, best of all, bottles and bottles and bottles and bottles of rice wine.

Curiously, the only person who didn't let his hair down and have a great time was the guest of honor himself.

After the 14th course and 33rd bottle of rice wine, the rest of us were three sheets to the wind. We began singing marching songs from our different basic trainings. I was laughing so hard I thought I would die. First, I led everybody in a chorus of that American favorite "Jody got hit by a claymore mine, doo dah, do dah, we wrapped his shrapnel-riddled guts and what little else was left of him in a body bag, doo dah, doo dah."

Then Trung led us in a South Vietnamese Army favorite "Ngyuen was decapitated by a B-40 rocket, doo dah, doo dah, we buried what was left of him in a poncho liner, doo dah, doo dah."

Trung was just about to lead us all in that oldy but goody, "The entire squad was incinerated when the truck ran over a command-detonated anti-tank mine with a white phosphorous core, doo dah, doo dah, we scooped up what was left of them in a canteen cup, doo dah, doo dah," when the division commander, who hadn't said two words all evening, got up, looked directly at me, and farted.

Most Americans would have taken this personally, but I didn't. First, he was facing me, so the Lieutenant behind him suffered the formidable fish-sauce-based blast. Second, this poor guy deserved some sympathy. He was really On the Spot with his Higher Headquarters.

Try as the General might, the 21st Division was still making consistent contact with the enemy, a condition which the South Vietnamese high command did not see as suiting the primary mission of their army, which was to be good hosts to the Americans and let them do the fighting, since they obviously wanted to fight, had come all this distance to do it, and seemed to get such a big kick out of it.

The poor 21st Division was like a broken record. The commander, whose name was Tho (pronounced "Toe"), would sit down with his Intelligence Officer, whose name was Pho (pronounced "Foe"), and try to find a place to go (pronounced "gough") where no VC in his right mind would be, since there was absolutely nothing of any value anywhere in the area. Then the 21st would go there and get absolutely hammered by the VC.

Some Vietnamese generals were calling Tho a "Hiep Tuop" (Big Dumb Turtle Turd) because he attracted VC the way turtle turd attracts flies. Others attached to Tho a truly devastating insult that qualified as a Low Blow by any standard: "Xien My Lo" (One Who Thinks Like an American General.)

If I had been in General Tho's shoes, with my nine-year-old son going to school and hearing his classmates call him a "ti ti Hiep Tuop" (a little piece of Turtle Turd that split off from the Big Piece Of Turtle Turd), I wouldn't have been in fine fettle, either.

Anyway, Tho kept looking steadily at me, and for a Vietnamese such continued eye contact was unusual. Then he gulped down another glass of rice wine, belched, farted once more (the Lieutenant behind him, who apparently lacked the good sense to come in out of the rain, went several shades whiter than I was) and began to speak.

"You know what you guys should be selling out here, instead of this 'defending democracy in the third world' shit, which even you don't believe, yet you expect us to?

"I'll tell you. You should be selling the Brooklyn Dodgers. That was the real America: Carl, Jackie, Pee Wee, Roy, Gil, the Duke............Ebbets Field on a Friday night in August........people of every race, color, creed, national origin, and sexual preference jammed in there elbow to elbow........ the Bums protecting a one run lead, Willy Mays up, tying run on third, first place on the line.......hot dogs, beer, little kids. Shit!, that was an America you could believe in, that was an America you could trust!

"Bhudda, you people had it all. No one needed a politician to explain what America meant. No one had to go to a shrink to understand the American Dream.

"And you fucked it all up. You let the Dodgers leave Brooklyn, the most American city, and go to Los Angeles, the least American city, just because L.A. is a better TV market."

At this point the General's pet parrot, which had been casting a baleful eye at me all night, swooped down, landed on my right shoulder, and doo-dooed all over my cleanest dirty uniform jacket. Pho continued without missing a beat.

"Didn't you people realize that every little Vietnamese kid on a water buffalo knew that the first person to break the color line in baseball, a color line that would never have existed if you Americans had believed your own bullshit, was a Brooklyn Dodger? Do you think it was an accident that it was a Brooklyn Dodger? Are you benighted Americans really so ignorant about the Cosmic Forces that control the universe that you sincerely think that Jackie Robinson just **happened** to be a Brooklyn Dodger? Are you people truly as dumb as you seem to be?"

The parrot slashed at my right ear lobe. I bled. The general rambled on.

"Do you really think that the great mystery of life can be reduced to nothing more than a profit and loss statement? Have you, a nation fathered by men who were fired with a great idea, become nothing more than slaves to your cars, color televisions, and tax shelters?"

The parrot stabbed at my cheek and—I could have sworn—called me a "phuop phap dang be Bong Xi My." (Imperialist Yangkhi Dog Brain who sucks turtle eggs). The general forged ahead.

"Have any of you people actually read the Declaration of Independence? Have you taken the time to listen to what that guy who was almost as ugly as you are had to say in that speech at Gettysburg?"

General Tho drank another glass of rice wine and went on. So did the parrot, this time aiming, successfully, at my nose.

"You let the Dodgers go and then you let them turn Ebbets Field into a housing project.

I was bleeding from at least three places now, but Pho was on a roll, as was the parrot.

"I'm telling you, when those crazy maniacs started the Viet Cong, I thought twice about joining. They might be rotten bastards, and if they win the war they'll fuck up this country worse than you people ever could, but at least they stand for something more than just taking the best deal and making more money."

Then Tho straightened up and said, "Gentlemen, a toast."

In an instant every Vietnamese in the room was on his feet and standing at attention, including Intelligence Officer Tho, who later turned out to be a VC, as did Trung's cousin and nine others in the room, including the two waiters and the parrot, who proved to be the cleverly disguised VC Deputy Commander of the infamous "Iron Pubic Zone," a rat's nest of bamboo and scrub brush that housed VC rest and recreation camps and was, not coincidentally, defended with unusual ferocity.

Even Trung, who, to say the least, was not a fanatic about military protocol, was standing at rigid attention, with a strange light in his eyes.

"To the Brooklyn Dodgers who once were, to the America that might yet be, and to the Republic of South Viet Nam that could have been, if only our world and yours weren't so often in the control of 'lien biets' (suckers of rotten turtle eggs).

Obviously, the So-Bo Theorem was not just a figment of a bar girl's fertile imagination.

Chapter 2
Our Hero Becomes Lost in the Loon Foon Forest, is Himself the Cause of Potential Disaster, but Fortuitously He Evolves a Plan to Avoid It.

Three weeks after the party, Captain Cohen called Sgt. Trung and me in for a briefing. Cohen was convinced that the Loon Foon Forest, a stretch of especially nasty jungle located next to the Dong Ding River, was a hotbed of enemy activity.

Higher headquarters and all Intelligence sources claimed that the enemy had been cleaned out of the Loon Foon by Operation Flagrant Misconduct, an ARVN-run, American-supported operation that had gotten huge press and great TV ratings (the Reverend Billy Graham made mention of it in his televised Sunday sermon). Accordingly, Higher Headquarters determined the operation to be a major victory.

But Cohen wouldn't buy it: "I'll make a second visit to a moil if there aren't VC under every bush in that forest." (A moil is the man who performs the ritual circumcision of Jewish males. While at West Point, Cohen had achieved a stunning upset in the finals of the NCAA wrestling championships by pretending that his undefeated opponent from Iowa State, a two-time defending national champion in the 167-pound weight class, was in fact the same gentleman who had "moiled" Cohen when he was an infant.)

I must add parenthetically that the Vietnamese bar girls, with whom I spent as much time as I could, which was never enough, claimed that not only was the Loon Foon full of enemy support personnel and major concentrations of food and ammunition, but it was also the rest area for the dreaded 274th VC Regiment, the "Yangkhi Bashers."

The 274th was an elite VC unit that accepted only volunteers who had passed the traditional Vietnamese manhood test of "phuoung suoung." Those willing to take this ultimate Bar Mitzvah first had to kiss a female water buffalo that was in heat. Those who survived had to steal the rice seedlings from a little old Vietnamese lady who wasn't blind. Anyone who could do both was considered tough enough for the "Yangkhi Bashers." I wanted to tangle with the 274th about as much as I wanted a root canal.

"But Sir," I said, trying hard to come up with a Good Reason for not doing this, "we have absolutely no hard evidence that there's anything in the Loon Foon but trees and bushes." Replied Cohen, with unassailable logic, "Of course, we have no evidence that the Congs are there. That's why I know they're there."

We went into the Loon Foon with a reinforced recon team of 15 men, 8 Vietnamese and 7 Americans. The helicopters dropped us off in one of the few clearings in the dense jungle. We quickly melted into the bush and, with Trung in command, began yet another walk in the woods.

Almost immediately things began to go wrong. There were signs of VC everywhere, and not just of logistical units. Our job was reconnaissance, not combat. Bar-room bravado was one thing, but no one wanted to bump into a main force Cong unit.

Trung was as nervous as I'd ever seen him. He kept saying that he had a bad feeling, and this pronouncement, coming from a man whom his fellow Vietnamese recognized as a "cua phua dua," made me more anxious than I usually was while on patrol, which was anxious enough. (cua phu dua: One whose appearance, language pattern, and socio-economic status give him an air of general disreputability, but who also for Buddha knows what reason sees things that the rest of us don't see and who often can tell that the water buffalo is going to experience a period of unusual flatulence even before the noxious gasses begin to gather in the animal's sizable gut.)

Trouble began the first night out. We were set up in the circular perimeter that the Zebra Force favored, with our feet in the center of the formation and our heads facing outward on the perimeter. We could hear the Cong moving about on beautifully camouflaged trails that even in the day were completely hidden from aerial observation.

Despite the presence of a large number of the enemy, the chances of our being found were minimal, since Trung had positioned us well off to the side of one of the smaller trails.

I blush to admit it, but I was the cause of the trouble that befell us.

The night before the patrol we had dinner at May Thi Lin's mom's hut. Mrs. Lin prepared us a real feast. There were piles of shrimp, mounds of rice, skewers of dog, gallons of soup, rashers of rat, plates of fruit, platters of fish, and, best of all, bowls and bowls of Mrs. Lin's justly famed fish sauce. Unfortunately, there was also a platter of hummingbirds, which the nice old lady had prepared in honor of her American guests. Of course, to be polite, I had to eat several hummingbirds, which I absolutely loathe because of the things they do to my stomach.

It was not unusual for me to have stomach problems while on patrol. I have no problem admitting that I was then and am now a confirmed wussie. (Let us remember that I was a member of the all-volunteer Zebra Force only because of circumstances beyond my control).

Some people sweat when they're scared to death; others get pale. I get stomach gas. When I was in Nam, I could usually control the gas, but that night I was having a difficult time, what with hummingbirds in my recent diet.

I fought the inevitable as long as I could, squeezing my cheeks together and trying to keep my mind off my churning tummy, first by contemplating the number of angels that could fit on the head of a pin, and then by pondering why angels would ever want to waste their time hanging out on the head of a fucking pin when they could have unlimited sex without the need of commitment or the fear of getting some foxy female angel pregnant, but...

phft.....pphhffffffft............ffffaaaarrrrtttt. Slowly and then more quickly, the truly noxious odor characteristic of a person afflicted with hummingbird flatulence began to drift off into the jungle night on a soft breeze that had just sprung up. (naturally, do I ever catch a break?)

The tension mounted. None of us was a rookie. We all knew what might happen next.

Off to our left we heard a Cong voice: "Chien phien le! Toi lien do luop-de. Hoa lien tran phuoc ky luop-de?" (Childhood memories! I smell a hummingbird fart. Did you candy asses in food supply manage to get your hands on some real food?)

 To our right, another voice responded, "Vien xien,luop-de? Con chuoc biet tay ky." (What'reyoufuckingcrazy, hummingbirds? The only meat we ever get is an occasional rat, and a tough one at that.)

Said the first voice, "Nu, lanh my co van tien ta, be toi bien toan luop-de." (Listen, man, I'm telling you, I smell a hummingbird fart just like my dear old uncle used to make.)

Responded the second Cong, "Phuoc! Dan phuong bo doi My! Di Di!" (Fuck! It's got to be an American patrol. Run! Run!)

The jungle around us exploded in activity as VC rice and ammo carriers took to their heels. Trung had us up and running in a second, hoping that in the general confusion we could get far enough away from the smell that had alerted the Cong so that the security squads which would arrive on the scene immediately would not be able to find us.

I struggled manfully to control my rumbling gut, but the exertion of running for our lives was too much: fhpht, fhlub, ffffaaaarrrrttttt. The tell-tale miasma floated behind us—behind me—as Corporal Cuoung caustically noted while wiping the sweat from his face.

And so began three days of constant running, fighting, fear, and farts. With Congs on our tails and trails, we couldn't slow down long enough to blast a landing zone in the jungle so a chopper could pull us out, and Trung wouldn't take us anywhere near the few clearings that a spotter plane found for us, because he knew the VC would have ambushes waiting at all of them. He thought that our only chance was to get to the Dong Ding river, hop in, and float downstream to a spot where we could be picked up by helicopters.

By the end of the third day we were almost out of ammunition and water. Miraculously, we had suffered no serious casualties, but the situation was desperate. The night before, a Cong had called out to us, "Fuck you, Yangkhi finkdogs. We bash you tomorrow."

Having exhausted his English vocabulary, the Cong in question continued to inform us in Vietnamese that a reinforced battalion of the 274th would soon arrive to destroy the egg-sucking, toilet-tongued imperialist running dogs (us Americans) and the egg-sucking, toilet-tongued puppet running dogs who ran with the egg-sucking, toilet-tongued imperialist running dogs (Trung and his men).

The morning of the third day brought with it more of the perfect "VC weather" that had plagued us: the cloud cover was so low you could touch it, and a hard, driving rain came down "like a water buffalo peeing on a flat rock," as Trung phrased it in a moment of exasperation. There would be no air support for us on what promised to be the last day of our last patrol.

With nothing to lose, we continued our run for the river, although all of us knew that any VC commander with a brain would, given the tactical situation, put a blocking force between us and the river. If he had, then we would be caught, with little ammunition, between the anvil of the blocking force and the hammer of the 274th, which was only a short distance behind us.

As we struggled through the jungle, a blast of automatic weapon fire sent us to the ground and let us know that the VC were indeed between us and the Dong Ding River, our only hope of safety. Trung, a professional soldier whose code mandated that he do it by the numbers even at the very end, sent scouts to the right and left, trying to find either the end of the enemy position or a hole in their lines where we could slip through.

The scouts reported back: no luck. We were cooked.

Trung ordered us to dig in and face in the direction from which we could expect our friends from the 274th. Even with nothing left except a final few rounds and then knives and rifle butts, there was no thought of surrender. Since the VC considered us Zebra Force soldiers to be "phien cuas" (phien cuas: unreservedly bad no-goodniks who would steal rice seedlings from blind little old ladies), anything was better than being captured.

We could hear the VC readying for the assault. We knew what we could expect, since the 274th always followed the same routine when attacking a dug-in enemy: first, a mortar barrage; then a volley of rocket-propelled grenades to take out the machine gun positions; then a swelling volume of increasingly negative commentaries about the parentage of people cursed by Heaven and forced to live within the city limits of Los Angeles; and finally the massed charge designed to overrun the Yangkhi position.

Then transpired one of those instants that make you wonder what It's All About. Lying there in a hole in the jungle, 8,000 miles from home, tired, miserable, about to get overrun by the Yang Khi Bashers, there came to me an instant of blinding, heaven-sent intuition: I remembered General Pho's's comment at his birthday party and I knew we had a chance!

Today, of course, I've read enough Rollo May and Carl Jung, watched enough Oprah Winfrey, and dated enough psychology majors from Long Island to realize that what I experienced in the Loon Foon was no big deal, just the falling into place of the last piece of a puzzle that my subconscious mind had been working on for a while.

Keep in mind that what I did was not as farfetched as it might seem, since we had no other chance of survival anyway. I never understood why they gave me a medal for it.

I stood up (behind a tree, of course) and, cupping my hands to form an ersatz bullhorn, began a re-created broadcast of that memorable, fateful, seventh game of the 1955 World Series, when life was simple, the Dodgers were in Brooklyn, where they belonged, and the only enemies worth hating were the eminently hateable New York Yang Khis, er, Yankees.

As all right-thinking Americans remember, the Brooklyn Dodgers were always breaking their fans' hearts by winning the pennant and then losing the World Series to the Yankees. All over the world, simple folk would huddle next to radios or sit glued to their primitive TV's and listen or watch as the Big

City Yankees, who always won everything, won the World Series yet again.

But in 1955, with the series tied at three each, God sent a sign that the Impossible Dream is not always a fantasy, and the Big City Slickers don't always win everything.

As a young boy who thought that the sun rose and set on Ebbets Field, I, along with millions like me around the world (including, I fervently hoped, many of the current crop of the 274th Yangkhi Bashers), had agonized through every inning of that game, waiting for the roof to fall in, as it always seemed to when you were a Brooklyn Dodger fan.

For three re-created innings there was not a sound in the jungle, except for my voice. In between pitches Trung would look questioningly at me and I at him. What was happening out there? Were the Cong gunners preparing to drop their rounds down the mortar tubes? Were the RPG launchers inching forward, ever nearer to our position?

Finally, in the top of the fourth the Dodgers scored on a Gil Hodges single, and from the jungle came a muted "Ja phai! Ja Phai! Mot cua chumg toi!" (Oh Yes! Oh Yes! That's one for the good guys!)

I was in a groove now, and both I and the game rolled on. With each Yangkhi out, cheers reverberated from both the 274th and the blocking force by the river.

In the top of the sixth a Yangkhi error ("Ja phai, hee hee, ja phai!") filled the bases and forced the withdrawal of starter Tommy Byrne, who had given up only three hits. Hodges drove in another run with a sacrifice fly. ("Ja phai! Ja phai! Hai cua chumg toi!") Improbably, the Dodgers led by two.

Then it was the bottom of the sixth, one Yankee on base and the hated, detested, feared Yogi Berra up. He hit a towering drive deep into the left field corner. As I described Berra's shot, I pulled out all dramatic stops: "Cai poouoong bien tay loc duop phiiiieeeennnn!" (That baaalll looks like it's goooonnnne!) When Sandy Amoros reached out and caught the ball just as it was going into the seats in left, the jungle rocked with "Tuan! Tuan! Ja Phai! Ja Phai!" (Fortuitous play! Fortuitous play! Oh Yes! Oh Yes!)

Then, to the beat of hands slapped against AK-47 stocks, the 274th began a rhythmic chant, "Giet ngui Yangkhis, giet ngui Yangkhis, phuouc phien loa ay con ngui my `schmucks'!!" (Bash those filthy Yankees, bash those filthy Yankees; fuck the excessively materialistic city of Los Angeles and all American schmucks responsible for the Dodgers' leaving Brooklyn!!)

The few people to whom I have told this story think that I exaggerate. They don't believe, for example, that the 274th actually sat there listening to a re-creation of a game when they already knew its outcome.

Ah, but to think this way is to ignore the essence of being Vietnamese and the essence of being a Brooklyn Dodger fan, two romantic world views which are remarkably similar.

The Vietnamese believe in a mystical power that translates into English, poorly, as "The Will of Heaven." Before you scoff, consider that for almost a hundred years the French had kept Viet Nam quiet with nothing more than a few soldiers and assorted colonial officials. French domination was, the Vietnamese would shrug, The Will of Heaven. Then Heaven changed its mind. Many Vietnamese pointed to the Japanese victories over Western powers at the start of World War II as the indicator that Heaven no longer accepted the dominance of Caucasians over Asians; after this sign neither thousands of French nor hundreds of thousands of Americans, nor their guns, planes, bombs, visiting celebrities, shells, or talk-show hosts could keep Viet Nam quiet.

So everyone in that jungle, Zebra Forcers and Yangkhi Bashers, knew that the Dodgers had won the 1955 game, but we also knew that, God being God and the Brooklyn Dodgers being the Brooklyn Dodgers, we weren't home free, even in a 1969 re-creation, until the final out, if then.

As we went into the seventh-inning stretch, Trung, calm and controlled as ever despite the intense pressure, noticed that the cheering and yelling from the VC blocking force had diminished, while the noise from the 274th position in front of us was growing ever louder. He surmised that the less disciplined Viet Cong of the blocking force had left their positions to join their brethren in the 274th for the dramatic final few innings.

Quickly, Trung sent a scout to see if we could slip through to the river. The scout reported that several enemy positions were now manned by only one or two soldiers, whose attention was almost completely focused on the game. We would certainly suffer some casualties in a breakout attempt, but the odds were good that some of us would make it to the river.

The problem was that I couldn't leave. With the game now in the bottom of the eighth and with Johnny Podres blowing his fastball by Yangkhi after Yangkhi, everyone, including the Vietnamese members of the Zebra Force, was hanging on my every word.

As Yangkhi first baseman Moose Skowron led off the bottom of the ninth, Trung moved quickly and spread the word that we would make our break right after the last out, hoping to be gone before the 274th finished the traditional Vietnamese post-game victory chant and Give-Thanks-to-Heaven cry.

Then there occurred something that I can explain no better now than I could then, which, come to think of it, is a statement I could make about that entire war.

In 1955, Yangkhi catcher Elston Howard had grounded to Dodger shortstop Pee Wee Reese,

who threw to Gil Hodges for the final out. In 1969
the ball took a bad bounce and skipped over Pee
Wee's head for a single. Yangkhi manager Casey
Stengel then sent up pinch hitter Sean Somerville,
who crushed Podres' first pitch into the centerfield
seats. The game was tied.

Tomb-like silence enveloped the Loon Foon Forest.
It had happened again. That damn Will of Heaven!

As the shaken Podres, who had celebrated his
twenty-third birthday the week before (which made
him older than most of us Zebra Forcers and
Yangkhi Bashers) got the third Yangkhi out, I
noticed a tear rolling down Trung's cheek.

In the top of the tenth the Dodgers threatened when
Pee Wee Reese was hit on the hand by a breaking
ball that didn't break. He went to second on a
sacrifice but stayed there as Duke Snider and Roy
Campanella fanned. ("Choi Duc! Tai sao 'Campy'?")
(Give us a break! What the hell's going on, Campy?)

As I announced Hank Bauer as the leadoff Yangkhi
in the bottom of the tenth, a growl of disapproval
rose from the jungle around us, the 274th being
aware that not only was Bauer a Yang Khi, but he
was also an ex-US Marine.

But then came a P.A. announcement that silenced
the muttering and grumbling: .... "Om, ba, co, tat
ca xi phan `Pee Wee Reese' kien, mot ngui Viet lo
sau `World Series', mot ngui Viet lo sau `les Bigs',

duop tam, Tam Ky `le quick', Hau Nghia ja phai, van co bo kien........ Nguyen Van Baaaayyyyy!"

(Gentlemen and ladies, now playing shortstop for the Dodgers in place of the injured Pee Wee Reese, this year the first Vietnamese ever to play major league baseball, now making the first appearance of a Vietnamese in World Series history, the Vietnamese Jackie Robinson, the pride of Hau Nghia Province, the favorite son of Tam Ky village, wearing the mystical number nine, a man who has always revered his ancestors, the Tam Ky scooter himself........ Nguyen Van BBaaaayyyyy!)

The Loon Foon exploded: "Phuop Nguyen, phuop Nguyen, giet ngui Yangkhis, giet ngui Yangkhis!" (Give 'em hell, Nguyen; give 'em hell, Nguyen; kill the Yangkhis, kill the Yangkhis!)

The Yangkhis quickly quieted the crowd by loading the bases with one out. After an infield fly to Hodges, Rizzuto came up: "...ky phuong lo tay duop sang! (... ground ball hit sharply through the hole and into...No! Bay goes to his right, backhands the ball, stops, thhrrooowws ...... he got him!)

My heart almost jumped out of my chest when a goodly number of the Yang Khi Bashers opened up with automatic weapons, but they were just firing skyward in celebration of Bay's great backhand stop and even greater throw.

On and on went this elemental encounter between life's fundamental polarities, encapsulated forever in the tangible symbols of the New York Yangkhis and the Brooklyn Dodgers. The noise around us was now constant: the stutter of automatic weapons being fired skyward alternated with expletive-loaded denunciations of the imperialist egg-sucking Yang Khis, shouts of encouragement for Bay and the other Dodgers, and more than a few prayers to Heaven for Just One More Run.

Bay led off the top of the sixteenth. In the twelfth he had brought the crowd to its feet when he muscled up on a hanging curve and drove it deep to center, but Vietnamese shortstops were not known for their power, and Bob Cerv, playing for the injured Mickey Mantle, caught the ball at the wall.

Now, with the entire Yangkhi infield watching out for the bunt, Bay laid down a perfect drag bunt and beat it out by a whisker. With the entire Yangkhi infield watching out for a steal, Bay stole second by a whisker. Then he went to third on a hit-and-run play when Furillo bounced to second baseman Bobby Richardson.

This was classic Viet Cong baseball, and the Yangkhi Bashers loved it: "Ja phai, Nguyen, ja phai, bang bong Chu Ho va Brooklyn!" (O yes, Nguyen, O yes, win one for Uncle Ho and Brooklyn!).

Roy Campanella came to the plate with one out and the winning run on third. By the time Campy had fouled off his third consecutive inside fastball, the count stood at two and two, and such a quiet had descended on the Loon Foon that you could hear a centipede drop into your foxhole. Everyone was locked into one voice:

"Phuoc-kien Yang Khi ca lo vinh, pouong....Bay luan..... ca lo diep loc loc, Bay sien vien .... Bay diieett bbooong!!!!!!!!!!! `Les Bums' mien phuan mot dien!!!!!! (The fucking egg-sucking imperialist dog of a Yang Khi pitcher checks third, stretches ..... Bay takes a lead ..... the egg-sucking pitcher delivers to ....!!! Bay is stealing home!!!, Yogi, who has the breath of a turd-filled turtle, blocks the plate, Bay slides ..... Bay scoorrees! The Bums lead by one!!!!!) Jubilation erupted.

In the bottom of the sixteenth the Dodgers needed only three outs to win their first World Series ever. Naturally, the Yangkhis immediately mounted a threat. Skowron doubled and went to third on a passed ball. Two walks later the bases were again full of Yangkhis. When Dodger manager Walter Alston replaced Johnny Podres with Clem Labine, the departing Podres was given a sitting ovation by both the 274th and most of our Zebra Force team.

Labine's first pitch was a fastball right down the pipe: "Phang rang Bing Bang!...Khomg! Bay bie bop, chuon, phling phlop, phuan `Gil", chumg toi hai!!!!!!!! Les `Bums' `numbah mot'!!!! (Line drive base hit up the middle! .... No! Bay makes a spectacular diving stab; he rolls over and touches second, scrambles to his knees, throws to Hodges; the ball is in the dirt but Gil scoops it out: we got a triple play!!!!!!!!!! Brooklyn, may Heaven smile on the

fairest of all cities, wins!!! The Bums are
Champs!!!!!!!!!!!)

This time the world exploded. The deliriously happy
Yangkhi Bashers let fly with every weapon they had.
Green tracers flooded into the sky and rocket
propelled grenades went whizzing through the air—
fortunately, over our heads and into the Dong
Ding—as the jungle rocked and rolled with cries of
"Di, Bay, di!", "Brooklyn dai biet!", and, of course,
the inevitable "Phuoc phien loa ay con Ngui My
`schmucks'!!!!" (Go, Bay, go!; Brooklyn forever!; and
Fuck the excessively materialistic city of LA and all
American `schmucks' responsible for the Dodgers'
leaving Brooklyn.)

In the ensuing wild celebration, we slipped through
the now entirely vacated positions of the VC
blocking force, jumped into the Dong Ding, and
floated off to safety.

Chapter 3
A Philosophic Time-Out as Our Hero Recounts Yet Another Hard-to-Believe but Totally True Story

Upon returning from a November 1969 patrol near the Dong Ding River, I learned that I had once again volunteered for service with the C.I.A. This single movement of a single soldier almost became one of those fulcrums of history (like Waterloo, Stalingrad, Madonna's "Like A Virgin" video, etc.) which the gods of Fate use to change the course of human existence.

The C.I.A. needed someone to debrief Chieu Hois. The Cheiu Hoi program was an initiative of the South Vietnamese government to encourage defections from the VC side to the government side. "Cheiu Hoi" loosely translates as "Open Arms."

In my first month with the C.I.A., drawing upon my experiences as a field soldier, spending hours in conversations with Cheiu Hois, using the C.I.A. reports now available to me, and listening to the bar girls with whom I spent a disproportionate share of my time, which was never enough, I made a wild—and absolutely correct—guess: I predicted the Met Offensive, the one desperate enemy ploy whose failure would have meant an American victory in Viet Nam.

In a December 1969 report, C.I.A. BuShRe 7041268910-06 "Cong To Launch Met Offensive," I claimed that intelligence analysts at all levels were wrong in interpreting the countrywide November-December decline in enemy activity as a sign that the enemy's political and military organizations had been decimated in the heavy fighting of 1968-69.

I noted that there was indirect evidence that the VC, most of whom shared the Vietnamese passion for baseball, had bet their entire treasury on a Baltimore Oriole victory in the recent World Series. The surprising, nay, astounding, N.Y. Met victory wiped out the VC bankroll.

I surmised that the enemy, far from being on the brink of military defeat, was simply broke, and had money neither for making capital improvements nor for paying personnel. It was therefore logical, I said, that the VC would launch a major offensive before the Super Bowl, capture large supplies of money, and bet everything on the outcome of the Super Bowl in a "Damn the torpedoes, full speed ahead" attempt to prolong the war.

The likely targets would be Thai and Filipino headquarters (Thailand and the Philippines had spontaneously volunteered to send troops to defend South Viet Nam after their leaders had deposits made into their Swiss bank accounts by representatives of an unnamed major power located south of Canada; the Thai and Filipino soldiers, who were not particularly interested in getting killed to make the world safe for political payoffs, and who were, like me, lovers rather than fighters, spent most of their time selling Almost Everything to

Literally Anyone, including the Viet Cong, and then using the money to buy Almost Everything at the American Post Exchanges ((PXes))), selected American officer and NCO clubs, clubs frequented by incredibly overpaid American civilian construction workers, and the homes of high level South Vietnamese government officials, all places where large amounts of illegal cash could be had.

I was absolutely right—and absolutely ignored. The furious Met Offensive caught us with our figurative (and sometimes literal) pants down. By the time we recovered, the VC had amassed huge quantities of money. The rest is history. They "bet the rice harvest," as the Vietnamese are wont to say, on the Kansas City Chiefs in the Super Bowl, and amazingly, the underdog Chiefs won. With the staggering sum of money now in hand, the VC insured that they could afford to prolong the war until American public opinion forced an end to U.S. involvement.

Editor's note: Fascinated by Puggelli's behind-the-scenes perspective on the Met Offensive and intrigued by the ex-sergeant's contention that the VC were somehow responsible for the Chiefs' 24-7 win over the Vikings, I contacted former Kansas City Head Coach Hank Stram and asked him if he and his staff had received any offensive or defensive suggestions from a 'neutral third party' before the Super Bowl. Said Stram, "I absolutely without reservation deny completely and totally anything and everything that is in any way, shape, or form, inherent in your base, vile, and disgusting insinuation that has no possibility at all of ever being even a little teeny bit true."

Part III, of which there are five chapters, each detailing a link in the chain of circumstances that comprise the core of the Amazing But Entirely True Story of how our hero ends up Partying With The Viet Cong and comes to know the enemy on a first-hand basis.

Chapter 1
Herein the Stage is Set for our Hero's Amazing Adventure

The only other time I've told this tale, there were several raised eyebrows, so I guess I should preface my story of the Annual Bui Mui Dui District Cease Fire and how I came to be the only American present at the Bui Mui Dui District Viet Cong Give Great Thanks To Heaven, Praise the Felicitous Memory of Uncle Ho; and Hook 'em, Horns; Root 'em out, Hogs; Get Down, Get Back Up Again Blowout Party and Rice Wine Bacchanal, with a little background information, just so you don't think I'm exaggerating a bit.

One fateful afternoon Trung and I were hanging out on the top of Nui Nui Nui Nu?

Nui Nui Nui Nu?, which, for the sake of brevity, I will henceforth abbreviate as "Nui Nui Nui Nu?", was a mountain on whose top the Zebra Force maintained an observation post/radio-relay station. Out in the middle of nowhere, "Nui Nui Nui Nu?" was a bleak, lonely hill nestled in a bend of the Dong Ding River.

(The translation of Nui Nui Nui Nu? is "Mountain (Nui) of the lickable (Nui has this adjectival meaning when pronounced with what Vietnamese linguists call the "falling rising falling rising tone") delectable virgin whose very appearance makes your heart melt in a way that is very similar to what you feel when you rise early and behold the sight of the

silvery grey mist curling from the shimmering
surface of the river in the first beautiful light of dawn
(Nui), but, meanwhile, can you believe the shit that
Heaven's dumping down on our heads these days
(Nu?)?)

It was the monsoon season. Every day, late in the
afternoon, the rain would come sweeping up the
river and fall upon us like a great silver-gray curtain
ringing down the day. We would all strip naked (I, of
course, would be naked except for Fred, my Bowie
knife) stand out by the perimeter wire, and take a
shower. Then it was time to dry off, get dressed,
and go into the command bunker for the evening
cocktail hour, which would officially commence
whenever Trung announced "Chi bhop phu dhu,
chumg toi la booze" ("Watch out mouth, watch out
tongue, watch out stomach, here it come.").

Anyway, one afternoon I was talking with Trung and
Thang and getting an early start on the evening's
cocktail hour. As Trung poured yet another round of
rice wine, I noticed a crowd of women coming out of
the village of Yoo Soo Moo—perhaps "boiling out
of" would have been more appropriate—and
heading towards our hill.

 Trung, the professional soldier even when relaxing
(unlike me, a professional relaxer even when
soldiering), was down the ladder in the blink of an
eye.

He had the other Zebra Force members in their
bunkers and had coordinated air and artillery

support before I finished my drink, grabbed an M-16, retrieved my Bowie knife from Thang, who had borrowed it to trim his toenails, gulped down Trung's drink, slung a grenade launcher over my shoulder, stuffed some grenades into my pockets, poured another glass of rice wine, strapped on the shoulder holster with the .38 that Uncle Rocco had given me as a graduation present from high school, dropped into its sheathe on my calf the throwing knife that my grandmother had given me as a going away present when I left for Nam, put on my mother's good luck medal with its picture of Our Lady the Extremely Militant Virgin, finished the bottle of rice wine, checked to make sure that the derringer that May Thi Lin had given me in honor of Gil Hodges' birthday was securely fastened in its wrist holster, checked to make sure I had finished the bottle of rice wine, and climbed down the ladder to meet what appeared to be a serious threat.

At best, it was a cleverly disguised VC attack. At worst, it was that most dangerous force on the planet: a horde of angry little old ladies. Thang, no fool he, yelled after me that he would stay in the tower and man the high ground.

Official American sources in Saigon listed Yoo Soo Moo as a "No Doubt About It, Unquestionably Pacified, Undeniably Friendly, Don't Even Waste Your Time Asking About There Being Any VC anywhere in the Vicinity." Sure.

Yoo Soo Moo appeared to be quiet enough during the day, which was the only time any of us went into

the village. Of course, we never went down in
groups of fewer than four, and four Zebra Forcers
carried a lot of firepower. What's more, even with
me in the quartet, three of the four were guaranteed
to be highly competent soldiers.

 And, unlike most other allied soldiers, Zebra
Forcers didn't generate needless hostility among the
civilian population, because none of us was dumb
enough to violate Zebra Force Commander General
Sy "Wild Sy" Siegal's rule for conduct in Vietnamese
villages: "Eat the food, don't diddle the young
women, tell the old women how pretty they are, tell
the old men how smart they are, and try not to be an
asshole."

In fact, because of the combination of my garrulous
nature, love of the local rice whiskey, a particularly
potent home brew, and ability to consume bowl after
bowl and plate after plate of the local cuisine, I was
somewhat of a favorite of the village little old
ladies.... except for Grandma Li, who would berate
me as I wolfed down her justly famed roast dog with
fish sauce: "Tien-Ti, gho di phai phap My. Quan doi
loc do boo doo." (No wonder you Americans can't
win this war. All you're good for is telling us how
pretty we are, which, between you and me, is a line
of buffalo shit that doesn't grow any rice seedlings.)

As luck would have it, the leader of the group of
village women was the aforementioned Grandma Li.
With the other little old ladies massed behind her,
she stood at the bottom of Nui Nui Nui Nu? and
yelled for me to come down.

By the time I negotiated my way down the rope ladder that served as the principal means of access to or egress from the hill's rocky summit, Grandma Li was, as my own grandmother used to say, "in Fine Fettle."

As I've readily admitted, I don't hear tonal differences so well when I'm excited or when the other person is excited (both conditions existed here), and this inability can cause some difficulty in a country with a tone-based language. At first, as incredible as it seems, I thought Grandma Li was saying, "The fucking Packers went for a touchdown in the third quarter instead of taking a sure field goal and they missed it and lost to the egg-sucking Vikings by one measly point."

I knew that Grandma Li was a die-hard Packer fan—she even had a picture of recently retired Green Bay coach Vince Lombardi in her hut next to her picture of Ho Chi Minh and her award as the 1967 Bui Mui Dui District Most Valuable VC Grandmother Mobilized Against the Yangkhi Dogs—but two things made me doubt my own ears.

First, the Armed Forces Network radio broadcast of the NFL Game of the Week, from which the VC did their Vietnamese language version for soldiers and civilians alike, was not scheduled until the next day; and, second, why would Grandma Li be talking about football when she was holding up a recently arrived citizen of the planet who obviously had a severe case of The Runs?

I finally realized that Grandma Li was telling me that this most staggeringly beautiful of all babies ever born on the face of this long suffering planet, this future solid citizen and superb soldier for Uncle Ho, this ineffably fantastic child who just happened to be her own grandson, had come down with Something Weird and was near death.

"Do something," she screamed at me. "Granted, you people can't win a war, you can't run your own country for shit, and you let the Dodgers leave Brooklyn, but you did invent football and baseball and you sent a man to the moon. Save my grandson." And she placed the infant in my arms, where the future VC promptly doo-dooed all over me.

Was I ready for this? Was I ready for any or all of this? No. But there you are and you have to do something. So I called for Trung to lower me a radio. Then I got on the horn to the chopper pilot who had delivered our weekly supplies not more than fifteen minutes ago. With luck, he could swing back around, pick up the kid, and get him to a hospital.

No luck. He had a priority delivery of ice cream and chocolate sauce for a press conference given by General Consternation in honor of the completion of Operation Existential Crisis III. But he did give me the call sign of another chopper pilot from his unit whose ship was in the air not far from our area.

I made contact and explained the situation and, like a fool, I told the truth, that the person in distress was an Indigenous Personnel and that there were no regular American ground forces in the area.

This pilot was one of those Americans who would not go out of his way if a Vietnamese was in jeopardy, particularly if said Vietnamese happened to be in an area not secured by American ground forces. Kindly Killer 2 (his call sign) radioed back that he wouldn't land, since our area wasn't secure.

"Not secure!" I said, "I'm in the middle of a clearing, in broad daylight, covered by enough firepower to destroy the city of Los Angeles, which, come to think of it, isn't such a bad idea, and surrounded by a bunch of Vietnamese little old ladies." I immediately bit my tongue, knowing that the last bit of information had without doubt convinced the chopper pilot that the area was not, in fact, secure.

In a fit of inspiration, one no doubt inspired by the angry countenance of Grandma Li, who looked as if she knew exactly what was transpiring—it always seemed to me that all Vietnamese understood English when they needed to—I said, "Hold a second, Kindly Killer 2," I have a Foxtrot Victor (friendly Vietnamese) here with me and he's trying to say something."

Holding the radio away from me, I said loudly, "Ding dong phluoc xi bang blang My a khomg ja phai bop bip rang pang!" Bringing the radio closer, I said, "The Foxtrot Victor says that if you don't land the fucking strange bird that make the sound like an Italian (the Vietnamese description of the 'wop wop' sound caused by a helicopter's rotor blades) and pick up the ineffably beautiful little boy who just happens to be the grandson of the duly appointed Chief of Bui Mui Dui District, who just happens to be me, a loyal supporter of the South Vietnamese Government and a good friend of General Tho, who is a good friend of General Consternation, I will so inform both the General, who will then inform the General, and the reporter from Time magazine who is doing next month's cover story on Pacified Villages and who is, not coincidentally, my hut guest."

No officer in his right mind—even a helicopter pilot—would knowingly offend a general and/or incur Bad Press, so Kindly Killer 2 radioed that he would swing back, pick up the sick child, and deposit him into a hospital. When I translated this for Grandma Li and the rest of the Yoo Soo Moo Village VC Ladies Auxiliary, there was a loud roar of approval and several choruses of "Dai phung te xau My sing anh loi pououng!!!!" (Long live the American neo-colonialist pig with the long nose that bends rather cutely to the right.)

Hindsight is, of course, perfect vision. But I remember thinking even then that this young lad was attracting an unusual amount of interest and concern, even given the combination of his precarious hold on life and the strong affection that the Vietnamese normally lavish on children.

When the helicopter landed, things got a bit tense. The transfer of the child from me to a crewman took place with no problem, but then Grandmas Li, who was unusually agitated, almost walked into the tail rotor—only my diving tackle saved her from certain death. "Boom bang phang rhang, Tien ti, choi duc!," she said. (Great hit, Tien Ti. You could be the strong safety for the Packers, and the way their secondary is playing this year, you probably should be.)

The chopper finally lifted off, and after giving effusive thanks and making many offers of heaping plates of shrimp and huge platters of dog, all washed down by bottles and barrels of rice wine, the little old ladies went back to the village. I breathed a small sigh of relief.

The next day Thang went into Yoo Soo Moo. When he got back to Nui Nui Nui Nu?, as we affectionately called Nui Nui Nui Nu?, he told me that the village grapevine reported that the kid had been close to death when he arrived at the Imperialist Fink hospital, but the Dog Brained Yang Khi doctors, fortunately, saved him. The young lad was now resting comfortably and would be released from the hospital in a few days. Thang also mentioned that Grandma Li had tacked up next to her picture of Vince Lombardi a crude rice paper drawing of an American with a big nose that bent to the right. This was a rare honor for, presumably, me.

Trung and I left that day for a two-week patrol into the Miasmic Swamp of No Return, a dismal place from which, thankfully, we returned, only a little worse for the wear.

The second we got back to Nui Nui Nui Nu?, Trung and I, along with Thang and Thuong, went into Yoo Soo Moo. After two weeks of Reconstituted Chipped Beef on Toast and Rehydrogenated Watery Eggs, it was time for plates of shrimp and mounds of dog, all washed down by barrel and vats and bottles and canteen cups of rice wine and other suitable potables (There are very few alcoholic potables that are not suitable).

As the four of us drew near to Grandmas Li's hut, she came rushing out, all smiles, and invited Trung and me in for a dish of dog. Simultaneously, her neighbor, Grandma !Phui!, equally all smiles, appeared and made the same offer to the two other Zebra Force members. Sensing a pattern of orchestration that indicated potential danger (lest you think me paranoid, remember that we had just returned from the Miasmic Swamp of No Return), I was already flicking off the safety of my AK—when Trung turned quickly to me and said, "Blop buop. Diet xong whong whang bhang." (Relax. I'll explain later. Trust me.)

Grandma Li plied us with succulent shrimp covered with mounds of rice, delicious dog swimming in her justly famed fish sauce, and oodles and oodles of rice wine. I was in Seventh Heaven, the rigors of the recent patrol all but forgotten.

As I reached for yet another bottle of wine, Trung and Grandma Li began a rapid-fire conversation that I could not follow, what with my bad ear and mildly intoxicated state. Given what was to transpire as a result of this conversation, it was probably just as well.

Chapter 2
Our Hero is Presented with a
Startling Proposal

The next night, I had the midnight-to-four radio
watch in Nui Nui Nui Nu?'s Command Bunker. At
1:30, Trung came into the bunker, sat down, and
began telling me about the substance of his
conversation with Grandma Li. I admit it, he
boggled my mind, a mind which had once been
easily boggable, but which now was—thanks or no
thanks to the war—was far less boggable. In
fairness, however, even the most difficult-to-boggle
brain would have been at least a bit boggled by
what Trung had to say.

First, let me give you the gist of Trung's startling
communication. Then, I'll attempt to put it in some
kind of reasonable context, although, God knows,
"reasonable" is not the first adjective I would choose
to describe what was being proposed.

Trung and I were being invited to the Annual Bui
Mui Dui District Viet Cong Cease Fire, Get Down,
Get Back Up Again, Rice Wine Blowout and
Bacchanal. The invitation was from the
Commander of the Bui Mui Dui District VC Main
Force Battalion, one Bay Vinh, who was the son of
Grandma Li and the father of the child whose life I
had been at least partly instrumental in saving. Bay
Vinh was also Trung's Best Friend and Worst
Enemy (a concept that is not at all contradictory to
the Vietnamese or the Sicilian mind) and had been

my partner's rival— obviously a successful one—for
the hand of Co Hoa, whom Trung described as "the
hottest little bod" in Hee Hoo Hai Village Junior High
School 103, Trung's Alma Mater.

Trung had, I learned, attended every Bui Mui Dui
District Cease Fire Get Down, Get Back Up Again
Blowout Rice Wine Bacchanal but one since 1962.
He spent the 1967 party in the hospital after he was
wounded by a VC booby trap. During the shop talk
that accompanied the hors d'oeuvres, it was
discovered that this booby trap been set by Bay
Vinh himself, a coincidence that caused gales of
laughter among the assembled and already
inebriated party animals, most of whom knew the
details of the Trung-Bay Vinh relationship/rivalry,
which stretched back to the days of their boyhood.

This year's event would be held on the day of the
Armed Forces Viet Nam broadcast of the Texas-
Arkansas football game, a climactic, end-of-the-
season matchup between the Number 1 and
Number 2 ranked teams in the country. Several
other Zebra Force members who had been born in
Bui Mui Dui District were also invited, as were a few
South Vietnamese Army soldiers. I was the first
non-Bui Mui Dui District native, and, of course, the
first American, who had ever been invited to this
event.

My understated response to Trung's figurative
bombshell was tempered by my desire to be
culturally sensitive and by my awareness of the
Vietnamese respect for conversational formalities

and love of linguistic circumspection: "Are you out of your fucking mind? Have you been caught in one too many mortar barrages?

"You want us—which includes me—to party with the hated, detestable, egg-sucking Viet Cong, those same fun-loving guys and girls who spend most of their time doing almost as good a job of dismembering, disemboweling, disabling, disfiguring, dispatching, destroying, deforming, demolishing, mangling, maiming, massacring, maligning, mortaring, machine gunning, maltreating, molesting, blowing up, bursting apart, rending, ripping, berating, butchering, bruising, booby trapping, shooting, slashing, chastising, crushing, rocketing, bombing, blasting, blitzing, crushing, crippling, stomping, sniping, pounding, pulverizing, terrorizing, torturing, impaling, incapacitating, incinerating, lacerating, stabbing, scourging, slaying, squashing, slicing, dicing, gashing, mashing, scorching, torching, ill-treating, misusing, abusing, confusing, harrying, hectoring, slaughtering, smiting, cleaving, cracking, shattering, scattering, and Wreaking General Havoc Upon us;

as we do of dismembering, disemboweling, disabling, disfiguring, dispatching, destroying, deforming, demolishing, mangling, maiming, massacring, maligning, mortaring, machine gunning, maltreating, molesting, blowing up, bursting apart, rending, ripping, berating, butchering, bruising, booby trapping, shooting, slashing, chastising, crushing, rocketing, bombing, blasting, blitzing, crushing, crippling, stomping, sniping, pounding,

pulverizing, terrorizing, torturing, impaling,
incapacitating, incinerating, lacerating, stabbing,
scourging, slaying, squashing, slicing, dicing,
gashing, mashing, scorching, torching, ill-treating,
misusing, abusing, confusing, harrying, hectoring,
slaughtering, smiting, cleaving, cracking, shattering,
scattering, and Wreaking General Havoc Upon
them?

"You want us—which includes me—to trust a
truce with those guys, the same people who are
notorious for General Sneakiness and Truly Dirty
Tricks, on which subjects they have forgotten more
than everyone but politicians, generals, lawyers,
and most of the inhabitants of Los Angeles will ever
learn?"

"Look," replied Trung, "don't get emotional about
this. Business is business: our job is to kill,
grievously injure, or cause grave and possibly
irreparable psychological damage to them, all in the
name of a nebulous geopolitical goal, and their job
is to kill, grievously injure, or cause grave and
possibly irreparable psychological damage to us, all
in the name of an only slightly more defined national
goal.   That doesn't mean we can't share some
social minutes together outside of work."

"Trung," I said, "you know I have great respect for
you and I love you dearly, but you're
absofuckinglutely nuts. There's a war on. Those
people are our deadly enemies. What's more,
they're Godless Communists and/or mindless
followers of the Godless Communists, which is just

about the same thing. Besides, since when have the Vietnamese ever been interested in college football? All you guys ever care about is baseball and maybe a little pro football."

"Listen," said Trung, growing a little angry, "if you Americans, who spent four years pounding the piss out of the Japanese, and then dropped two atomic bombs on them to boot, can turn into a nation of sushi lovers, and if the Japanese, who spent four years pounding the shit out of you, only to get two atomic bombs dropped on them for their troubles, can be mature enough about the whole thing to invite American baseball players to play for Japanese teams, then why can't you and I take time out from this fercockta war and partake of a good time that I guarantee will curl your toes? There will be enough rice wine there to float the fucking Titanic."

"Rice wine?" I said. "Did I hear rice wine mentioned?" The possibility of an unusually good party had its usual soothing effect on me. "OK, OK, I understand why they invited you. You grew up with those guys, and if a Sicilian, even a half breed like me, understands anything, it's that blood is thicker than water, except of course when business dictates that it's not, but then that's OK, because business is business, or, as Uncle Rocco puts it, 'Business is always business, unless it's personal, and personal is never business, unless, of course, it is, and then it's personal business, which, of course, means that you can't take it personally, but if you didn't take it personally, you should have,' but why do they want me there? Don't give me that bullshit about Bay Vinh being grateful because I saved his kid's life. You Vietnamese are like Sicilians and American politicians: the first reason you give to someone to get them to do something is guaranteed NOT to be the real reason you want it done."

"Well, to tell you the truth," Trung said, "Bay Vinh does feel a certain debt to you because you saved his kid, but there is more to his invitation than simple gratitude, which, after all, more often than not just gets in the way of business. The translator who's supposed to do the play-by-play commentary of the Texas-Arkansas game was captured by one of our patrols last week. Bay Vinh has requested another translator from Higher Headquarters, but the VC chain of command isn't a whole lot more reliable than ours, so Bay wants you there just in case. His people have piles of money bet on this game, and they don't want to take a chance that they won't be able to follow the action."
"Will there be any food?" I asked.

"Does a hobby horse have a hickory dick?" Trung responded. "Every year the menu gets bigger and bigger. There will be scads of shrimp, dozens of dogs, mound of rice, bowls of soup, vats of fish sauce ...."

"Grandma Li's fish sauce?" I interrupted.

"Does a water buffalo shit in the jungle?" Trung said.

"Are you telling me the whole entire unvarnished truth?" I asked.

"Have I ever lied to you?" he said.

"Yes," I said. "My first patrol with the Zebra Force you said it would be a piece of noodle and we spent nine days in the Valley of the Big-Breasted Woman getting the absolute living shit shot out of us."

 "Well, besides that."

"My second patrol you said we'd be out for one week and we spent 17 days in the Bang Bing Woods."

 Trung countered, "Have I ever lied to you any more than your trusted elders, respected role models, teachers, religious persons, government officials, and other assorted authority figures have lied to you?"

He had me there.

Chapter 3
Our Hero Prepares to Get Down and Then Get Back Up Again

Between you and me, I had been playing Devil's Advocate with Trung on one important point, i.e., the Vietnamese, especially the North Vietnamese, growing interest in football: I had heard barroom conversation in Ebbets Field on the subject of North Vietnamese Commanding General Vo Nguyen Giap's fascination with certain elements of American collegiate football, especially the option play.

In fact, if you asked me—and of course no one did—Giap had based his pre-Tet Offensive military strategy on the same principle that is fundamental to the option play, which is to accommodate one's offensive maneuvering to the defense's response to your initial gambit, and in the process to pit an offensive strength against a defensive weakness.

For example, the basic play in the wishbone option offense works like this: the quarterback takes the ball from his offensive center and seemingly commits the ball to the fullback, who runs a direct route at the defense to either the immediate right or to the immediate left of the quarterback. If the strength of the defense closes on the threat created by the fullback, the quarterback pulls the ball out, continues his own lateral movement along the line of scrimmage, and either keeps the ball himself and attacks the defense or, if he is in danger of being tackled, pitches the ball to a trailing halfback, who is often in a position to exploit the largely unprotected perimeter of the defense, since a number of the defenders have committed themselves to stopping the fullback and the quarterback, who do not have the ball. Of course, if the strength of the defense does not close on the fullback, preferring instead to protect the flanks, the quarterback allows the fullback to keep the ball and to attack a now undermanned interior defense.

To a complex, sophisticated man like General Giap, who had to command an army against an enemy with overwhelming technological superiority, it was eminently logical that one should adopt an offense that accommodated itself to the structure of the defense and thereby created a situation where the weaker side's strength could be matched against the stronger side's weakness. Someone like Giap, an Asian man and an intelligent one, would have immediately seen that the spirit of the option play is, philosophically, far more Eastern than Western.

Giap's pre-Tet Offensive strategy bore all the characteristics of a masterful option play: first, he mounted a threat to the Marine garrison at Khe Sanh, drawing the attention of the American High Command, press, and public to the danger at Khe Sanh (by analogy, the threat of the fullback); the US High Command then committed its technological, psychological, and numerical strength to maintaining the safety of the beleaguered Khe Sanh garrison; Giap then unleashed the full fury of his offense on the unsuspecting and largely unprotected cities (which is, by analogy, the pitch to the trailing halfback; which is also not a bad capsule summary of the Tet Offensive.).

If General Eastlessland had not committed massive air and artillery support to the Khe Sanh garrison and had not positioned large American ground forces within quick relief range, I'm sure that Giap would have launched a serious assault upon Khe Sanh itself, a tactic that could have resulted in Touchdown, Fullback.

Besides the natural compatibility between the spirit of the option play and the genius of Vo Nguyen Giap, there was another factor of relevance here. In May Lin's words, "The North Vietnamese are far more anal than we Southerners, and it's only natural that they should like a violent, brutal game like football, while we Southerners naturally prefer the more poetic game of baseball."

Of course, this breakdown was no more or less true than any other essentially sound generality. There were VC who were football fanatics, and there were North Vietnamese—Giap among them— who were fascinated by the life-within-a-game, game-within-a-life ebb and flow of baseball. Not to mention that a large number of Southern Viet Cong, who had gone North right after the Dodgers' shameful exodus from Brooklyn, had inevitably picked up some local customs during their sojourn in the North. When these individuals went South again, to become the heart of the nascent Viet Cong movement, they brought these new customs and interests back home with them.

The Texas-Arkansas game just happened to offer the kind of symbol-fraught matchup that would appeal to the VC, or for that matter, to almost any Vietnamese. The ground-oriented Texas attack featured the wishbone option offense, which encapsulated a flexibility that, as I have said, the Vietnamese psyche, or at least some Vietnamese psyches, found to be "simpatico."

The Arkansas offense, a version of the Power I formation that relied more upon brute power than flexibility, could easily be seen as an analogy for the American way of waging war, especially as Arkansas immediately resorted to its powerful air attack when its ground game began to sputter. Clearly, the contest could be viewed as the football equivalent of the Vietnam war.

Of course, this actually <u>being</u> the Viet Nam war, the situation was more complicated. The Arkansas team symbol was a hog, and many VC who had been born in the North, where hog raising was more common, had a strong emotional identification with the "Razorbacks," as they were known, because of the deep-seated Vietnamese respect for and belief in the power of symbols. Many native Southern VC had an equally strong feeling toward the Texas mascot, a Longhorn, because this beast bore, especially after several glasses of rice whiskey, a passing resemblance to the sacred water buffalo, indispensable to the wet-rice agriculture that was more common in South Vietnam.

So, to make a long story short, one could predict that a group of party maniacs composed of Zebra Force members, VC who were native Southerners, and VC who were native Northerners would definitely be both pro-Texas and anti-Arkansas and pro-Arkansas and anti-Texas. The key question was who would be in what group. The only way to find out the answer was to go to the party.

Chapter 4
Our Hero Gets Down and Then He Gets Back Up Again

The unofficial Cease Fire officially began at 3 AM. At 3:30 Trung and I set out from Nui Nui Nui Nu?, heading northwest into the Long Bong Special Zone, the home of the Bui Mui Dui District Viet Cong headquarters and the stamping ground of the District's Main Force Battalion. I, of course, was following Trung. Having inherited my father's sense of direction, or lack thereof, I was completely lost after two steps into the jungle.

 Two hours later Trung suddenly stopped, peered through the jungle gloom, squatted, and handed me his canteen. "Drink," he said.

I unscrewed the canteen's top and immediately smelled the unmistakable aroma of Satchel Charges. "Isn't carrying a canteen full of Satchel Charges to a District Cease Fire Bacchanal a little like bringing your own bottle to a bootlegger's wedding?" I asked. "What about the gallons of rice wine we're going to imbibe in what is, I hope, the immediate future?"

"Trust me," Trung said. "You're going to need a bit of a buzz before we get to the rice wine."

"Never let it be said that I ever needed anything more than a poor excuse to ingest a suitable potable," I said, tossing down a healthy belt of Satchel Charge.

"Have another one," Trung said. And so, of course, I did.

Then Trung stood up and stamped his foot on the ground three times.

I almost jumped out of my skin when two feet from me a Vietnamese suddenly popped up from a hole in the ground that hadn't been there a second ago.

"Chao, Trung, xi phi My, dhong bhong bhing?", said the Vietnamese, who was obviously a VC. (Hey, Trung, you old-dog brain puppet of the American pig-breath Imperialists, how're they hanging?)

"Chao, Linh, dhong bhong bhig bhing, le pham rang Cong," responded Trung. (Hey, Linh, they're hanging just fine, you godless and mindless minion of Moscow.)

Trung said to me, "Knock down another Satchel Charge and let's go. We've arrived at Party Central." He then followed Linh down into the mouth of what was apparently a cleverly disguised tunnel. From beneath the earth I heard Linh's voice: "Noi phuoc My tien tieu anh lop." (Tell the Imperialist Buffalo Breath with the exceedingly strange nose to pull the door shut after him.)

Let me tell you, I sucked down that entire canteen of Satchel Charges on the spot. The only thing I knew for certain about Viet Cong tunnels was that I certainly didn't want to be sober in one of them.

The hole into which I crawled was not, if one were to be technical about it, a tunnel, per se. It was an entrance to a shaft that went straight down for about four feet and then met a real tunnel, which joined the entrance shaft at a right angle, like an "L". Crawling on our hands and knees, Trung and I followed Linh, who lit the way with a flashlight. Trung, the eternal Boy Scout, was of course as prepared as ever and had brought his own flashlight.

We followed Linh for what seemed like a long time. However, I must admit that I'm not particularly good at estimating time when I'm crawling on my hands and knees in a Viet Cong tunnel, with a bit of a buzz on from a canteen full of Satchel Charges, trying not to notice the crawly little and not-so-little things that waved their arms and legs—or perhaps they were legs and arms—at me.

After a while Linh dropped down through another trapdoor into another vertical shaft that was joined at its bottom by another tunnel, and we began the whole process again. This tunnel, however, was larger and more substantially constructed. I could almost move at a crouching walk, although that would have meant chancing contact with the furry whatevers that hung from the ceiling and made nasty spitting sounds if one came near them.

After one more trapdoor and one more shaft, we were into a serious tunnel whose hard-packed dirt floor showed signs of heavy traffic that included wheeled vehicles. How far beneath the surface we were I didn't want to know, especially with the Satchel Charges beginning to wear off. Fortunately, I could finally see a light at the end of the tunnel.

When we got to the source of the light, which proved to be several bulbs that bespoke a generator somewhere, we found a large room. I'm 6 feet tall, and I had to extend my arms to touch the ceilings in this room, which held, of all things, a printing press. Besides the printing press, there were layout tables, about 40 trays of type, a table with bottles of ink and dyes in 5-gallon cans, and tables with stacks of pamphlets and this week's issue of the Bui Mui Dui District Will of Heaven Weekly.

While Linh paused to speak with the paper's Art Director, I picked up a copy still damp from the press and learned that Grandma Li had once again won the annual Bui Mui Dui District Most Valuable Grandmother Mobilized Against the Yang Khi Dogs Award. Also, the paper's pigskin prognosticator had Arkansas favored by a touchdown over Texas because she thought that Hogs were cuter than Longhorns. Women.

I was just beginning Grandma !Phui!'s feature article on How to Booby-trap Your Own Booby-Traps when Linh finished his conversation and we were off again.

Linh lead us through another, smaller, room that contained several of the famous "Dien Bien Phu" stoves that I had heard about from the bar girls at Ebbets Field. Named after the great Vietnamese victory against the French, these virtually smokeless stoves had been specially adapted for use in tunnels. What little smoke they did produce was ducted through several channels and finally allowed to escape from various and separated ground level chimneys. By this time the smoke was so diluted that it was barely visible.

If my nose did not lie to me—and whatever else one could say about my nose, even my worst enemies gave me credit for a superior sense of smell—one of the cooks was preparing a grilled rat. As I went from stove to stove conducting a sniff search for this delicacy, to which Trung had introduced me during our involuntarily extended, patrol in the Bhig Bhang Valley, I noticed that someone had entered the kitchen from the other side. Instinct told me that this gentleman, who was carrying a tray with two large glasses on it, was the famous, or infamous, Bay Vinh.

"So, Trung," Bay Vinh said in flawless English as he handed me a glass of rice wine and then gave one to my partner, "we've managed to make it through another year of unparalleled absurdity. Unfortunately, the same can't be said for many of our friends."

"Nu, diep lop khe, 'Nhu anh, nhu bhoo'," said Trung, quaffing a good half of his drink. (Well, you know the old saying, 'Another year, another Multiple Fragment Wound.')

"Still the cynic, eh, Trung?" Bay Vinh said. "By the way, aren't you putting on weight? Life with the Imperialist Dog Brain Egg Sucking Yangkhis—no offense, Tien Ti—must suit you."

"Fuck you and the water buffalo you rode in on," Trung replied, switching to English and quaffing more of what was a particularly potent batch of rice wine. "I weigh exactly what I weighed last year, which was exactly what I weighed when I took you downtown when we were in high school."

"Which was exactly what you weighed when I took Hoa away from you," Bay Vinh retorted.

I gulped down my rice wine, having learned that Bay Vinh knew my Zebra Force nickname and having resolved that during the party I would learn more about the incidents to which the two close friends/bitter enemies had referred.

"So," Bay Vinh said, turning to me, "tell me, Tien Ti, do you think that the ultimate significance of the option play, which is of course a metaphor for how each of us must accommodate our life to the Will of Heaven, is ontological, epistemological, or phenomenological?"

"Definitely," I countered. "So, are these rumors of barrels and vats and tubs of rice wine just another

Foul Communist Deception, or are we actually going to get down to some serious partying, or what?"

Just then our philosophic discourse was interrupted as a small Vietnamese child, carrying what looked like a crude imitation of a football, came scurrying into the room on his short little legs, shouting "Chu Bay! Chu Bay!" (Uncle Bay! Uncle Bay!) Trung swept the boy up in his arms, causing the football to fall to the ground. At the time I could have sworn that this fumble elicited from Bay Vinh a muted "Choi duc di bop nam muoi an lac le 'pill'." (I've told the kid 50 times that you can't drop The Rock.)

With Trung carrying his nephew, whose named was Nguyen and whose father, mother, two sisters and brother had been killed during the bitter fighting of the Tet Offensive, we went from the kitchen through a short tunnel and into the main party area, where the party committee composed of VC and Zebra Forcers were putting the finishing touches on what had clearly been an elaborate preparation.

"We're using the small room this year?" Trung asked. "Yes," Binh responded. "Every year there are fewer and fewer of us."

"Didn't you invite the North Vietnamese?" Trung asked, referring to the North Vietnamese soldiers who had been attached to VC units to make up for the large numbers of native VC that had been killed in the Tet Offensive. Bar room rumor had it that the VC in Bui Mui Dui District had suffered relatively few casualties during Tet, in no small part because of

Vinh's leadership. However, given that many VC units had been decimated, "relatively few" still meant casualties in the 40% range. I knew that Captain Cohen was sure that some North Vietnamese had been attached to Vinh's command, although he didn't know how many.

"Of course, I had to invite them," Vinh said, but, Thank Buddha, most of them refuse to sit down and engage in non-Marxist decadence with Pawns of the Fascist-American Military Industrial Complex. I'm telling you, those guys are anal."

I was fascinated by this behind-the-scenes look at the tension between the North Vietnamese and their Southern cousins. Gulping down more rice wine, I listened eagerly as Trung said, "Anal ain't the word for it. Remember in '66, when you had to invite that Commo Liaison cadre from Hanoi, you remember, the one with the gorgeous set of ...."

Trung was interrupted by Nguyen's shouting that he be put down, whereupon the tyke ran furiously around the room, jumping over bottles of rice wine, dodging around of members of the party committee, and ducking under tables.

"How old is he," I asked Vinh.

"Four," he said.

"Kid has some size on him for four."

"He's going to be bigger than either his father or his mother, may Heaven care for their spirits."

"He's got quick feet. How's the hand-eye coordination?"

"Excellent. The hand-eye coordination and the quick feet he gets from our side of the family; the quick feet come from his mom."

"Kid grows up, he'd make an option quarterback."

"Could be, could be."

Life is such a trip, even in the middle of a war. If you had told me then that I had just had the conversation that would be the major turning point in my life, minus the booby trap I stepped on not exploding, I'd have laughed in your face and told you that you couldn't handle your rice wine. But there it was.

Just then we heard a loud "Chuop phuop! Le khot!" (Watch out! Hot Stuff) and waiters began coming out of the kitchen with steaming platters, which they set on tables that ranged along the sides of the room. During the ensuing lull in the conversation I looked around at Party Central.

At the front of the room were tables on which rested barrels, bottles, vats, and tubs of rice wine and rice whiskey. A short distance from the booze supply the presence of a miniature rice paper Hog seemed to indicate a squatting section for the Arkansas fans,

as a small—and, to my mind, shoddily
constructed—rice paper Longhorn on the other side
of the room did for Texas supporters. On a table in
the middle of the room rested a huge pot of
something that gave off the unmistakable odor of
Grandma Li's justly famed fish sauce!

When the waiters had cleared out, Vinh led Trung
and me to the back of the room, where we checked
our weapons in the cloakroom. While I was
shedding my grenade launcher, grenades, .38,
throwing knife, derringer, Bowie knife, AK-47,
straight razor, .45, brass knuckles, garrote, and
Swedish K, I noticed that the cloakroom held
nothing but M-16's and M-79 grenade launchers,
hardly standard issue for the Viet Cong. Later in the
evening Bay Vinh would tell me that these weapons
had been purchased from the Quartermaster of the
ARVN 21st Division, who was not a VC but who had
read Catch-22 and who was adamant that the
novel's real hero was Milo Minderbinder, a
conclusion confirmed by his growing bank account.

After we got our claim checks, Vinh led us to what
were clearly Seats of Honor, right in front of the
table bearing Grandma Li's fish sauce. Next to our
rice paper mats were a bottle of rice wine, a bottle of
rice whiskey, and a paper plate loaded with
hors d'oeuvres. Without further ado, we sat, Trung
on Vinh's right and I on his left, and began
alternating shots of rice whiskey with draughts of
rice wine and bites of tasty Dong Ding River shrimp
dipped in fish sauce.

While we were priming our pumps, as Trung would say, more party animals began to drift into the room, check their weapons, get some booze and food, and find a squat in the rooting section of their choice. As far as I could tell, the breakdown was about 80% VC and 20% Zebra Force/South Vietnamese Army. Minus Vinh himself, there didn't seem to be an officer in the place, although with both the VC and the Zebra Force it was difficult, if not impossible, to distinguish officer from enlisted man by appearance, behavior, insignia, or conversation.

Just then Vinh's wife, Hoa, came in to say hello to Trung, meet me, and collect little Nguyen.

Hoa rated an 11.5 on a 10-point scale. Trung, unflappable even under the heaviest incoming fire, was obviously a bit flapped by Hoa's unexpected appearance. His uncharacteristic taciturnity in her presence, especially at a party, made me even more determined to plumb the depths of my partner's tale of love-lost woe.

Hoa's departure with Long was the signal for both the beginning of serious drinking and for the onset of that male shop talk that flourishes best in the absence of women and children, even if the kid is the nephew of one of the province's most respected/detested Viet Cong leaders, and the woman is a fully accredited guerrilla fighter with a specialty in Squad Size Ambushes and a sub-specialty in Political Assassination/Random Terrorism.

I was trying to keep one ear on Vinh's animated conversation with Trung and one ear on the chatter that flowed from the Texas and Arkansas rooting sections.

.......and so Vinh—you remember Vinh, the one with the cross eyes who can't stop shitting every time he hears a helicopter—he was supposed to lead a punishment raid on this hamlet that was getting too friendly with you puppet bastards and the Yangkhi fucks; so the night before, he and his men drink some rice wine that had gone bad, and the next day everyone is hung over, so they decide to have some of the hair of the dog that bit them, and by the time they get to the hamlet they're supposed to trash, they're all potted, and Vinh, who was supposed to order his men to shoot the water buffalos and rape the women, he gets confused and tells them to shoot the women and rape the water buffalos, and I heard that you couldn't tell who was more pissed off, the women or the water buffalos, and all you could see was assholes and elbows and water buffalos all over the place, and the women wiped out damn near half of Vinh's men and the water buffalos got most of the other half........

......say, Thanh, where's Hoang, isn't he coming?.....

.......nah—you didn't hear? Last month he was sawing open unexploded bombs that you shits drop on us all the time, Hoang, he was really good at it, too, in fact it was Hoang who sawed open a couple of 500 pound bombs and got the stuff that we put in that command-detonated mine we used last June to blow your cousin and his men to dog meat; anyway, this time the bomb he was sawing on went off and Comrade Hoang was blown into more pieces than even Heaven could count......

.....too bad.......

.... not really, I mean, we all have to go someday, and Hoang was always bitching, and you know how Hoang could bitch, about how the thing that scared him more than anything was getting hit by napalm or run over by one of your tanks and not dying right away, so in a way he was lucky...........

.... hey, Phung, I heard that somebody messed up a platoon of the Large Crimson One by sneaking in at night and turning their claymores around so that when those idiots fired them during your attack they blew up in their faces..... was that you?......

.....yes, it was child's play. I don't know where those Yangkhis belong, but it certainly isn't in the jungle.............

......Trang, you misbegotten offspring of a diseased frog and an ugly toad, isn't the Yangkhi fuck who's talking to Trung and Comrade Vinh the one who saved your worthless and foul smelling ass in the Loon Foon Forest by doing that broadcast of the Dodger game?.....

.... yeah, I was shitting bricks this big that day, let me tell you. The 274th had us by the balls ....

......I bet you didn't hear what happened about a week later; half the 274th wanted to mount an attack to capture Big Nose so they could make him do the game again whenever they need a morale boost, and the other half wanted to send one of our Special Assassination Teams after him so there would never again be a chance that our soldiers would be manipulated into not doing their Revolutionary Duty, which is to destroy the enemy—especially you fucks in the Zebra Force—whenever possible.

.....so what happened?......

..... nothing, the 274th got wiped out in a B-52 raid......

.....life's a bitch, my respected but ideologically obtuse former classmate....

.....too true, my esteemed but politically naive ex-friend, and then you die, but in the meantime there's always rice wine to get us through the night.......

Just then Vinh got up, climbed up on the table that held Grandma Li's fish sauce, and called for everyone's attention. I knew what was coming next. Get a Vietnamese a little plotzed and the next thing you know it's toast after toast after increasingly sentimental toast full of Great Ideas that Will Never Happen On This Planet. Romantics are all alike.

"Beloved friends, detested enemies, on this most Special Night I propose a toast." Instantly every Vietnamese in the room was on his feet, with me only a fraction of a second behind.

"To a time when life was simple, to a time when we were all friends—well, Trung, at least most of us—to a time when young men were able to write poetry to their young ladies and to ponder the mysteries of the Will of Heaven, instead of having to devise new ways of blowing our fellow human beings into dog meat." Vinh paused, his eyes filling with tears, as, I confess, were mine, mushy sentimentality being, after all, catching. "To," his voice wavered, "to a time when The Dodgers Were in Brooklyn."

With a loud "Ja phai!" (Damn straight!) we all guzzled down whatever we happened to be drinking, which in my case was a bottle of rice whiskey.

Vinh climbed down from the table and was replaced by Trung.

"To Hoa, may this often ugly world in which we all must live someday become as beautiful as her soul has always been."

Another chorus of "Ja phai's" was followed by more sounds of gurgles and guzzles.

I'm usually a little quiet at parties held at the underground headquarters of people whose avowed purpose is to fragment my body into as many pieces

as possible, and to induce significant pain in the
process; and normally I wouldn't have done what I
did, but I had just finished a bottle of rice whiskey on
top of a vat of rice wine on top of a canteen full of
Satchel Charges.

When Trung got down, I jumped up and said "To us,
to all of us who have to fight this fercockta war, to us
Dog Brain Yangkhis, to you Running Dogs of the
Pig Breath Imperialists, and you Godless and
Mindless Minions of Moscow. If our leaders spent
more time drinking rice wine with each other and
eating grilled rat smothered in Grandma Li's justly
famed fish sauce, then people like us would have to
spend less time blowing the shit out of each other,
and then we all could instead blow the shit out of the
city of Los Angeles and all those worthless fucks
responsible for letting the Dodgers leave Brooklyn!"

The place went nuts. Repeated "Ja phai's"
alternated with shouts of "Noi ban dia lien, Tien Vi!
(Tell it like it is, Big Nose) and several "'Fercockta' la
gi?" (What the hell does 'fercockta' mean?)

On and on it went, toast after increasingly
sentimental toast, shout after even louder shout,
gurgle after increasingly deeper guzzle.
Vietnamese being Vietnamese, this could easily
have gone on all night, were it not for the kickoff of
the Arkansas-Texas game, which was rapidly
approaching.

Chapter 5
The Game

With kickoff 5 minutes away, the room began to return to some semblance of order, with the Arkansas fans back in their squatting section, the Texas fans in their area, and Trung, Vinh, and I, along with several other VC, ensconced before the vat of fish sauce, each of us with a plate of munchies and several bottles of our favorite potable.

Bay Vinh and I hadn't said much to each other yet, save for some pleasantries, and I knew that I hadn't been invited just because of my good looks. As several of his men were setting up speakers in the corners of the room, he said, "Who are you rooting for, Tien Ti," he paused, looking at me from behind half-closed eyelids, "and who are you betting on."

Impressed once again by how similar Vietnamese and Sicilians were, or at least how similar Southern Sicilians and Southern Vietnamese were, I said, "In this case my heart and my wallet are in agreement. Texas will win, although I won't be surprised if Arkansas is ahead at the half and possibly into the fourth quarter. The Hogs have considerably more talent than Texas and they'll shut down the Wishbone in the first half. But if Texas is persistent, and doesn't lose faith in the Wishbone, they'll get back in the game in the second half, although their coaches will have to make some adjustments and combine a little passing with the Wishbone."

"No! No! No! Never! Never! Never!" screamed one of the VC who had joined us—the only one, by the way, who was without a suitable potable. "The Wishbone is a brilliant concept! It is ideologically sound! It has been lauded by Comrade Giap himself! It is unstoppable! It is the perfect vehicle with which to express Revolutionary Fervor! It is pure! It is magnificent!"

"Anal," I heard Trung mutter, "anal."

"What did you say, Imperialist Puppet?" shouted the VC, whose more guttural accent identified him as a North Vietnamese South Vietnamese.

Attempting to defuse a volatile situation, Vinh edged closer to me, began rubbing my arm (a common practice among Vietnamese males) and asked me what changes I had noticed in myself since I had come to the war.

Like a true Sicilian, or, for that matter, like a true Vietnamese, I answered his question with an irrelevant story (the Greeks invented this form of communication; they called it "Philosophy"; the Sicilians stole it, adapted it in their own unique way, and call it "Extortion"; wives have raised this custom to an art form and term it "talking to your husband when you're not interested in having sex"): "When I was a senior in high school, I took this course called 'The Literature of Gloom, Doom, and Depression,' and we read a book by this German. It was a story about a guy named Gregor, who wakes up one morning and finds out that he's become a bug. I used to think it would be disgusting to wake up and find out you were a bug, ugh! Now, I wake up some times and I wish I were a bug, so I could crawl off somewhere and not have to worry about booby traps, ambushes, RPG's, snipers, snakes, rockets, jungle rot, mortars, and anything I don't want to deal with, which is most of what I have to deal with on a daily basis."

"Kafka!" "Metamorphosis!", Vinh said. "I read him when I was in Hanoi.
Did you know that Kafka stole the idea for that story from a Vietnamese?"

"No!" I said.

"Seriously," he said. "In 1896 Nguyen Van Hien wrote a short story with a character called Huyghen, who wakes up one morning and finds that during the night he's become a Phuyghen."

A Phuyghen (the word, which is pronounced "phuh-yen"—and which, curiously, rhymes with Huyghen, which is pronounced "huh-yen"—translates as "stinking spitter") is a particularly nasty-tempered, remarkably ugly, and exceedingly foul smelling frog. As I can attest from personal experience, the Phuyghen had the irritating habit of hopping up to the edge of a foxhole early in the morning and spitting upon the inhabitant thereof.)

Vinh continued, "The story of Huyghen the Phuyghen is quite similar to the story of Gregor the Bug. In each case the family is appalled by, and refuses to accept, the horrible thing that has happened to their loved one, although, between you and me, they were at least indirectly responsible for it. I mean, we don't exist in a vacuum, do we? The Bell doesn't Toll for no one, does it? Anyway, as both characters begin displaying the behavioral characteristics of their respective life forms, they become increasingly isolated and alienated.

"But there is a major difference between the two stories. In Hien's story, there is a Wise Old Man in the village who drinks a gallon of rice wine and then goes to sleep. While asleep, he has a dream during which he consults with his ancestors and learns what to do to restore Huyghen to his original form. When the Wise Old Man awakes, he tells everyone in the village about his dream and there is General Rejoicing. Then the entire village accompanies the Wise Old Man to where Huyghen is sitting, perched on a rice paddy dike and spitting at and occasionally on passersby. 'Huyghen, Huyghen,' says the Wise Old Man, 'it has been revealed to me how I can cure your afflictions and turn you back into a normal Vietnamese farmer.'

"But Huyghen the Phuyghen, instead of hopping for joy, spits at the Wise Old Man, hitting him with a rather large frog goober, and then hops off into the jungle and lives out his life there, happily spitting at, and occasionally on, everyone and everything."

Vinh went on to tell me that the Vietnamese of 1896 interpreted Huyghen's action as a bold statement against the French Colonial presence and a clarion call for Vietnamese independence. "Huyghen the Phuyghen" societies sprang up in every Vietnamese hamlet and village. Throughout Viet Nam young men would, Huyghen-like, hop up to the village Wise Old Men and spit on them, calling them "Uncle Nguyens," because they had accepted French domination.

Author Hien became a national hero and was accordingly shot by the French, which made him even more of a national hero, and so the French dug him up and beheaded him.

As I remember Kafka's story, nobody gives a damn about Gregor the Bug, and he dies. Existentialists throughout the Western World interpreted this ending as a sign that death is bad, especially if you had been born, and that anyone who dies is therefore stupid, and since everyone apparently dies, everyone is therefore stupid, and life, especially for rich people who have the time to think a lot, is consequently without meaning.

Call it what you will—I attribute it to the huge volume of alcohol I had consumed—but, squatting in an underground room in the middle of the Long Bong Special Zone, I shed a tear for Gregor the Bug, who got even less sympathy than a soldier in an unpopular war, and voiced a silent "Ja phai!" in memory of Huyghen the Phuyghen, whose attitude to Wise Old Men I found laudable (Uncle Rocco, of course, excepted.)

As a general comment upon the rest of the evening, I must say that Vinh, whose soldiers had raised the jungle ambush to an art form, was himself the master of the Philosophic Ambush. For example, "Tien-ti, have another shrimp, and, by the way, don't you think that in the classical conception of Being there exist at once the ontological problem of the modal distinction of the real world and the epistemological problem of objective reality?"

Or, "Tien-ti, pass the rice wine, and do you agree that our ability to question the existence of the Will of Heaven is a phenomenological confirmation of Its existence?"

Or, "Have some more fish sauce, Tien ti, and while we're on the subject, do you think that warfare is the result of logic that is intent upon evil or is it rather the result of the absence of logic?"

(For the record, my responses were "Yes," "No," and "Yes," respectively. As the nephew of Rocco (The Truly Big Fink) Bovino, I knew well enough not to walk into philosophic ambushes prepared by a romantic with a cosmological bent.)

The more perceptive and experienced Vietnam scholars who are reading this have undoubtedly already deduced what I later learned but had not yet grasped: Bay Vinh was no ordinary middle-level manager. But more about this later.

The game developed as I had predicted. Arkansas, having little respect for the Texas passing game, committed virtually all of its defensive resources to the line of scrimmage and throttled the Wishbone, which caused Comrade Bo, the North Vietnamese South Vietnamese, to weep and wail and gnash his teeth, in addition to making entirely inappropriate comments about what he was going to do to a particular part of my anatomy once the cease fire was over.

The Arkansas offense, mixing the pass with the run, moved up and down the field. But critical mistakes—or mistakes at critical times, a nuance that Vinh noted, drawing analogies to Waterloo and Gettysburg and quoting Sun Tsu, Machiavelli, Hobbes, St. Thomas Aquinas, and Yogi Berra— bedeviled the Hogs, and their second-quarter touchdown, which inspired riotous celebrations and toasts in the increasingly inebriated Arkansas rooting section, was the only score of the first half.

As far as I could tell, the VC announcer, who was doing his translation straight from an Armed Forces Viet Nam radio broadcast, was doing a reasonably accurate and objective job, minus his tendency to editorialize during time outs. I doubt, for example, that the fans in the students' sections in Little Rock, Arkansas, were holding up signs that read "Long Live the Glorious Memory of Uncle Ho" or "Get Out of Viet Nam, You Egg-Sucking American Soldier-Finks." Then again, 1969 being the strange year that it was, maybe the translator was accurate.

It being halftime, I of course had to make the obligatory trip to the latrine. When I asked Vinh where the architect had placed the Facilities in this underground maze, he pointed to the back of the room, where a sign that read "Cau Tieu" (Latrine) hung just to the left of the cloak room. Under the sign was a tunnel that branched off from the Main Party Room and led to a much smaller room that was laden with the scent of many a bladder's ferment. Each toilet was a jar buried in the ground. Squatting over one of them, I voided my inner pouches, as Trung was wont to put it, or I did a number one followed by a number two, as we used to phrase it at PS 143 in Bay Ridge, Brooklyn.

As I was finishing up, Vinh came in. "Don't you think," he said while squatting, "that there is some philosophic significance to the fact that whether we're capitalist or communist, our shit still smells the same?"

"Do you believe," I countered with an old conundrum, "that if someone takes a shit in the middle of the jungle, and then continues down whatever trail he's traveling on, that the shit doesn't smell because there is no one there to smell it?"

"Tien-ti," Vinh chuckled as we finished our business and went back out into the tunnel, "except when you're talking about the option play, you're the most close-mouthed American I've ever met. Why is that? Don't you have a Weltanschauung, or is it just that you're a Sicilian?"

"Where does that tunnel lead to?" I parried, pointing to a narrow passage that branched off to the right about halfway between the latrine and the Main Party Room.

"I'll show you," Vinh said, leading the way. This tunnel was so narrow that we had to go single file and on our hands and knees. Fortunately, when we crawled into what was obviously our destination, I could rise almost to my full height. "This is a very special place to us," Vinh said. As my eyes fell upon a sign that hung on the wall near the entrance door, I could venture a guess why: this was the "'Campy' Luong Phuot" (The Roy Campanella Memorial Room).

Of course, as every person of sound character knows, Roy Campanella was the All-Star catcher on the Brooklyn Dodger team that won the 1955 World Series. Partly because he was a man whose race had been excluded from The Bigs because of skin color and partly because he played a position with which the average Vietnamese could identify (catching being a down-in-the-dirt, keep-right-after-them job, much like farming), Campanella, or "Campy" as he was called, ranked only behind the legendary Jackie Robinson in the eyes of Vietnamese baseball fans.

When That Terrible Day came, and the Dodgers abandoned Brooklyn and went to That City, there occurred within Vietnamese society those repercussions that led inevitably— as I had learned already—to the formation of the Viet Cong and to the war itself.

But Vinh told me what I had not known: shortly after word was received that the Evil Deed Was Done, an old Vietnamese from Can Tho, a respected Phien Cua named Old Van Phu the Respected Phien Cua, drank two quarts of rice whiskey, went into a trance, and announced that Heaven was opposed to this unnatural deed that had been done to Viet Nam's Team. Moreover, as a manifestation of Heaven's power and Displeasure, neither Jackie Robinson nor Campy would ever play for the Los Angeles Dodgers.

When Robinson retired rather than play on the West coast, heads wagged and tongues clucked in many a Vietnamese village. But when Campy was seriously injured in a car accident—the injury would confine him to a wheelchair for the rest of his life—the Vietnamese reaction was composed partly of sorrow for an innocent man who had been singled out by Fate and largely of an awareness that this Fate had made the Will of Heaven known in a way that no self-respecting Vietnamese could misconstrue.

"And so," Vinh said, "this room is our way of remembering Campy as a good man, one whose life was unalterably changed by the decisions of other men, who did not even know him and who, worse, did not even know themselves. This is a fate that all us soldiers can understand. And, of course, we remember the Lesson that Heaven made clear to us. No matter how long it takes, no matter how much suffering is demanded of us, we will fight on to The Final Victory."

"Vinh," I said, "whether your side wins or my side wins, people like you and me usually lose. If the VC and the North Vietnamese manage to kick us out, I'll lay odds that the VC come out with the short end of the stick. Two minutes after the first tanks roll into Saigon, Hanoi will take over the government and you'll be assigned to tending sugar cane stalks in the Miasmic Swamp of No Return, assuming, of course, that you survive that long."

"You might be right about that," Vinh said. "The North Vietnamese aren't particularly big on my act even now. Comrade Bo thinks that I'm unorthodox, which most North Vietnamese consider to be a greater faux pas than farting in the presence of your mother-in-law, and Higher Headquarters puts up with me only because I get results and they need me. But I'm not talking about the war. I'm talking about The War."

"Huh?", I said.

"Come on, Tien-ti, you, of all people! The War! The Great Struggle! The Protracted Conflict!" Vinh drew himself up to his full height, which, given that he was Vietnamese, wasn't all that much. "The Brooklyn Dodgers will rise again!"

"Vinh, you do one hell of an ambush, you plant a mean booby-trap, and you throw a great party, but you don't know Americans for shit. The Dodgers moved to LA, may my tongue rot off for pronouncing the name of That Place, and that's where they're going to stay; Ebbets Field is a housing project, and

that's what it's going to be, despite all the good
wishes in the world.   It's the American way: money
talks and nobody walks."

"'Money talks and nobody walks?'" Vinh said.
"What does that mean?"

"Beats the hell out of me," I said. "It's what my
Uncle Rocco always says. The Bottom Line is that
the Dodgers aren't ever going to play in Brooklyn
again, except in our fantasies."

"Tien-ti, you can't let life make you into a cynic."

"I can't let life make me into a cynic??????", I said.
"Are you fucking nuts?????? I mean, I spend my
time trying to mangle, mutilate, and maim my fellow
human beings, of which you are one, all the while
trying to avoid being mangled, mutilated, and
maimed by these very same fellow human beings,
of which you are a very dangerous one, in order to
Make The World Safe For Democracy, and even I
have to admit that what we're defending here isn't
exactly democracy at its best, or even at its worst,
and no matter what General Eastlessland and Billy
Graham say, we probably won't win, and not
winning is almost as bad a sin in America as not
making more money than your best friend, unless,
of course, you're screwing your best friend's wife,
and even if we did win, it would probably in the long
run be worse for us than if we didn't, and even if I do
manage to survive with my body and spirit relatively
unscathed, or as unscathed as someone like me
can ever be, given that I was pretty scathed to begin

with, all I can reasonably expect in return is to get to go home and be called all sorts of names by my peers, family, and friends, while I'm not being given a job by people who think it's pretty gauche to go around mangling, mutilating, and maiming people, unless, of course, you win or make a lot of money in the process, or, preferably, both; and to be given a lot of reasons why I shouldn't be bothered by it all, since I must clearly be one of America's Least and Dullest, or I would have found a way to use The System to beat The System, which is what all good lawyers and Ivy League students do, and I wouldn't have had to go to Viet Nam anyway, and To Top It All Off, the Brooklyn Dodgers, the team that represented everything that America was supposed to stand for, get moved to Los Angeles, pptttuuii, the city of Big Boobs and Bigger Bucks, and you squat there and tell me that I shouldn't let life make me into a cynic?"

"You're so American," Vinh said.

"What the hell," I responded, "even though you're a Vile Communist, when you're right, you're right. I sound like a North Vietnamese or a White Anglo-Saxon Protestant who works on Wall Street and lives in Westport. I mean, what we're doing is a matter of Life and Death, but is that any reason to be grim? Let's party."

When we got back to Party Central, the halftime was almost over and, if one was to believe the translator, the Arkansas band was just finishing up its rendition of "Liet Ba Hau Muong Xi Phuop"

(There Must Be More to Life Than Rice Wine and Women, Honored Mother, But I Haven't Found It Yet, And, To Be Honest, I'm Not Really Interested in Looking.).

Dipping another shrimp into the vat of fish sauce and opening another bottle of rice wine, I settled down to enjoy what was obviously going to be an exciting second half.

The Texas Wishbone continued to sputter, Arkansas' offense continued to move up and down the field, and their second touchdown made the score 14-0.

"Perhaps Texas should try another offensive formation," Vinh said. Even Comrade Giap admits that the Wishbone isn't a good catch-up offense as long as you Americans insist on playing football games by the clock."

"Good point," I said, "and if I were coaching Texas I would use a modified form of the Wishbone."

"Heretic! Deviate! Unorthodox Person! Scum! Cretin! Revisionist!" screamed Comrade Bo, "To modify the Wishbone is to be a Big Fink!"

"Explain to me what you would do differently," Vinh said, drawing closer to me and keeping Comrade Bo, who was verging on apoplexy, away from me.

Taking some notepaper from my pocket, I began drawing x's and o's and showed Vinh the offense I had developed during Religious Instruction class when I was in high school. I called this offense the Veer because the angle of attack of its basic play had the running back "veering" to the outside of the defense rather than moving straight ahead at it.

The Veer, like the Wishbone, was based upon the principle of the option play. But, because of changes in the offensive backfield— my plan called for the removal of one running back, who was replaced by another wide receiver—the Veer option offense could produce a much greater passing threat than could the Wishbone. The combination of the option play and a legitimate passing attack would prevent defenses from ignoring the threat of the pass and committing The Kitchen Sink to stopping the option attack, which is what Arkansas was doing to Texas.

"Brilliant! Masterful! Logical! Philosophical," Vinh said. "You should be a football coach, in the unlikely event you survive and go home."

"Nonsense," I said, "I'm going to work for my Uncle Rocco and get rich."

"Who can predict The Will of Heaven?" Vinh said, just as Texas scored its first touchdown, cutting the score to 14-6.

"If Texas is smart," I said, "they'll go for two points now, when the pressure isn't so great. If they get the two, then they can win the game by scoring one more touchdown and kicking the extra point. It's psychologically easier to get a two-point conversion earlier in the game than it is at the end, when the pressure is intense."

Texas made the two-point conversion, and the score was 14-8.

As the fourth quarter began, the tension mounted and the rice wine flowed like water. Arkansas couldn't score again, but neither could Texas. Finally, with the game's final minutes ticking away, Texas began a Desperation Drive.

At the 50-yard line, Texas was stopped cold on a third down play and faced a fourth and one.

"What would you do?" Vinh asked me.

"It is obvious what to do!", yelled Bo. "Follow the instructions of the Central Committee! Be Orthodox! Give the ball to the fullback!"

"I'd fake to the fullback and throw to the tight end," I said, ignoring Bo and downing another glass of rice wine. "The defensive back covering the tight end will be influenced by the fake to the fullback and he won't be able to cover the tight end on a pass."

Which, in fact, is exactly what transpired. The resulting 32-yard gain caused pandemonium in the Texas squatting section, whose inhabitants immediately began to sing the Texas fight song, whose strains did not prevent Comrade Bo from hearing Vinh's muttered "Phuoc My tanh sau!" (This in one fucking smart American!).

Now inside Arkansas' 20-yard line, Texas reverted to basic Wishbone football. With the threat of the option play keeping the outside parts of the Arkansas defense honest, the Longhorn quarterback repeatedly gave the ball to the fullback, who pounded into the line and edged ever closer to the goal line.

The noise, at least the noise in the secret underground headquarters of the feared Bui Mui Dui District's Main Force Viet Cong Battalion, was incredible, with the Texas fans shouting "Go, 'Horns, Go! Win one for Uncle Ho!" and the Arkansas rooters screaming "Booby-trap that line, and, if necessary, shoot the fullback!"

With seconds left on the clock, Texas scored, kicked the extra point, and won, 15-14. Half the room was jubilant; the other half was in despair. Football is like that.

Part IV: Our Hero spends his last weeks in the war, engages in some Philosophic Introspection with his Boon Companion, and plays a key role in the Battle of the Big Breasted Woman.

Joseph M. Puggelli

Chapter 1
Wrestling with Heaven

As Trung and I sat in the command bunker of Nui Nui Nui Nu?, I could see that he was in a funk, and for reasons that went beyond the noxious fumes that filled the bunker. I had eaten hummingbirds again, at a sort of going away party Grandma Li had given for me. I was due to leave country in 15 days, a departure that filled me with indescribable elation and a nagging sense that I would miss Trung and our rice-wine-fueled flights of philosophic fancy. His uncharacteristic mood, which I partially attributed to my imminent departure, had been exacerbated several days ago, when we were on R&R in Down Me Throut, a rest and recreation center on the South China Sea. Captain Cohen sent us there after a particularly difficult patrol south of Fire Base Inveterate Nihilist, which lay in the heart of the Valley of the Technical Virgin.

The villa in which we stayed in Down Me Throut was surrounded by a walled compound, and had a front yard with real grass and a fountain in the middle. A mother duck and her brood of newly hatched ducklings resided in the front yard, and Trung and I enjoyed sitting on the verandah, Satchel Charges in hand, and watching the mother waddle around the yard, followed in lock step fashion by her babies. I had to admit it: the baby ducks were cute, and cuteness had not been present in large quantities in the Valley of the Technical Virgin, or anywhere else we had been in a long time.

On the third day of our leave we noticed that one of
the baby ducks seemed to be having a problem:
when his brothers and sisters changed direction,
following their mom as she zigzagged about the
yard, this duck would stumble and fall as he
attempted to change directions.

On the morning of the fourth day, the duck's
condition was worse. He could only run about ten
or fifteen tiny duck steps before he would fall over
on his left side. Then he would struggle back to his
feet, and try to catch up with his family, but of
course he would only go a little bit and then he
would fall down again. His family seemingly took no
notice of him. It was obvious that the little duck had
either been born with or had suffered some
neurological damage.

When we came out on the verandah after lunch, I
could see Trung searching for the disabled duck.
When he couldn't find him, he asked the
groundskeeper, who told him that the duckling had
died.

As I was downing yet another Satchel Charge, I was
surprised to notice a tear on Trung's cheek. "Tai
Sao, Tien-Ti, kien phu 'le s___' lam nao? Mot
phoung bhang lop. Hiet phai? " (Why, Tien Ti, does
Life have to be so full of shit? The duckling did
nothing to deserve such a Fate. And why did his
family show no concern for him?)

Even though I had been raised as a male in a
Sicilian household, and was therefore Completely

Self-Absorbed and Generally Ignorant of the Needs of Others, I was capable of recognizing a moment of deep and powerful introspection such as the one afflicting my good friend and Boon Companion.

In fact, although I had no intention of talking about it, I had recently had one such moment, at Fire Support Base Utter Disillusionment, in the Valley of the Technical Virgin.

Captain Cohen had volunteered me to talk to a prisoner in whom Higher Headquarters was interested, and so I was picked up by a chopper on the top of the Hill of the Limp Member and deposited at the artillery base, where the prisoner had been part of an NVA assault team the night before. Supposedly, came the message, this prisoner had Said Something in a language that sounded like Russian. The Powers That Be were concerned that he might be a Russian adviser (There had been credible reports about Caucasians carrying weapons and serving with enemy units, and it was possible that there might be Russian advisers in close-to-the-Cambodian border areas like the Valley of the Technical Virgin, which was of great strategic importance because of the positioning of the Hill of the Limp member, astride, if such be the correct term, the approach to the Technical Virgin's entrance.)

One look at this particular prisoner, however, was enough to confirm that he hadn't been speaking Russian: first, he was clearly Vietnamese; second, he had no jaw and no tongue, having been shot in the face. How such a report had even been generated was Beyond Me. All I can say, is Stuff Like This happened, and not infrequently.

I sat and looked at him and he sat looking at me with blood dripping from the bandage that covered the ruin of his life and suddenly I Felt Weird, even though there was absolutely nothing strange or weird about what was going on.

So I empathized with Trung, to the extent that someone like me can empathize with another human being (which is on a par with the degree to which a Senator Gives a Shit about what his or her non-corporate constituents really think), but I also realized, as Uncle Rocco would put it, that the duck was dead, screw it, Drive On, and let's party.

"Come on, Trung," I said, "you have to stop feeling Down in the Dumps. I'll tell you what: Let's have a party tonight and get drunk."

"How's that different from what we do every night when we're out here?" he replied

"Let's have a fake battle tonight, and this time no one will get hurt. We can get plotzed, sit back, relax and watch the fireworks."

"How?" said Trung, suspiciously.

"Simple," I said. "We'll have a late cocktail hour, and after the first round of Satchel Charges I'll call the artillery people and tell them our Nixon and

McCarthy sensors have picked up enemy movement."

"What enemy movement?" he retorted. "Those fercockta sensors haven't picked up anything since those idiots from Higher Headquarters had us put them out there, and after you talked to Captain Phung, we know why."

"You know that and I know that, but Major Hyperbole (the commander of Fire Support Base Kneejerk Reaction, the artillery base that supported Nui Nui Nui Nu?) doesn't know that, or anything else, for that matter. He'll be happy because he'll get a chance to fire his Big Guns. We'll be happy because we'll get to see some great fireworks, and no one gets hurt. What, I ask you, could possibly go wrong?"

I can't believe I said that.

Chapter 2
Events Conspire Against our Hero

What we didn't know then, and what we found out
from a prisoner only after the fact (the fact being
what the VC called the Battle of the Big Breasted
Woman (Their code word for Raquel Welch), what
the Zebra Force knew as the Non-Battle of Nui Nui
Nui Nu?, and what the Americans called the Battle
of Hill 560), was that, even as we were downing our
first Satchel Charges of the evening, the VC were
Pissed and were planning Something Bhig for that
night, and their target was us.

Truth to tell, once we found out the whole story from
the prisoner, it was difficult for me and Trung not to
sympathize with them: had we, and especially
Trung, been in their place, we'd have been similarly
pissed.

According to the prisoner, many VC, weary from
years of fighting, depressed by the prospect of
years of more fighting, under constant air and
artillery bombardment, increasingly under the
influence of the harder-edged Northerners, having
to go without sex (a consequence both of the
circumstances natural to guerilla warfare and of the
North Vietnamese belief that something as fun as
sex had to be against some Party rule and was
therefore banned as counter-revolutionary ((except
for the Bhig Shots, who, much like their American
counterparts, were under such Great Pressure to
Make Rules that the rules they made naturally didn't

apply to them))) and often forced to live in tunnels for increasingly longer periods of time, were Down in the Dumps.

A local commander, Do Thang Thuong, had an idea. He ordered one of his agents, who was a bar girl at a club that catered to soldiers from the 201st, to steal a copy of a Truly Bad Movie with one redeeming characteristic: it starred Raquel Welch, with whom (or, to be more precise, "with whose boobs") most VC were as infatuated as was Trung.

Commander Thuong's plan was to show the film on a Saturday night, under the triple canopy jungle. The projectionist would turn down the sound (Most VC didn't care about the dialogue in "Fathom" ("She's a sky diving darling built for action.") and those attending would be carefully schooled to make no noise in order to frustrate the Nixon sensors which the VC knew to be in the area; all attendees would be equally schooled to think No Bad Thoughts, thereby frustrating the McCarthy sensors.

Rice wine would flow in abundance; Raquel's formidable assets would be on the screen for an hour and a half, providing tangible— if not, by the precepts of Western reason, entirely logical—proof that Heaven does in fact exist, and a good time would be had by all, especially, the prisoner would tell us, by Commander Thuong.

Thuong had his eye on Hai Lo, a delectable sniper/81 millimeter mortar person from Hee Hai Ho village, whom he had invited to the event, and with whom he planned to engage in Hanky Panky, his first in over three years.

It was in fact Hai Lo who was the unwitting cause of the disaster that followed. As the crowd was settling in, watching several shorts before the main attraction (including the now mandatory North Vietnamese "Sleeping with your AK-47: A fun exercise in revolutionary discipline," with subtitles, for silent viewing), Hai Lo looked around, and, fresh from a mortar attack on a unit of Screaming Hummingbirds and the assassination of two South Vietnamese government officials, she had a moment not unlike the one Trung experienced at Down Me Thruot: "Hoa binh phai?" she thought. "Bhai lup my duop? Xien phi hien?" (Aren't people more important than ideology? Why must we do these terrible things to the Americans and their turtle-sucking puppets and why must they do the things they do to us. Can't we all—communist and capitalist, Asian and Western, yellow, black, brown and white —just get along?)

The sweet, young, but quite naive Hai Lo had just Phoucked Up, Big Time: a McCarthy sensor in the area immediately picked up such an Un-American and therefore Communist thought pattern, the American monitor miles away quickly noted the target coordinates, and within seconds artillery rounds began dropping on the assembled VC, who, with characteristic discipline, quickly dispersed to their tunnels. Unfortunately, a direct hit from a shell

destroyed the film, the projector, and the
projectionist.

At that point, said the prisoner later, Thuong "nuop
duop" (lost it.)
He was enraged because now he would not get to
see Raquel's boobs, he had lost his golden
opportunity to do Visual Reconnaissance of Hai Lo's
smaller but much more available boobs, and he
would have to fill out reams of paper explaining the
destroyed projector and film (the influence of the
much more anal and form-loving North Vietnamese
was beginning to manifest itself within the VC chain
of command).

Thuong, deep in "nuop duop," was in that state
which Uncle Rocco describes as "mafiya" (the
condition of "huhnh!!!!," an anger that passeth
bounds that even a Sicilian male would consider
reasonable).

When the barrage was over, Thuong assumed that
the cause of the artillery fire was a Zebra Force
recon team (he never even considered that one of
his own men/women, as thoroughly trained as they
were, would set off a McCarthy sensor). He had his
men get three little items he had "borrowed" several
months ago from a North Vietnamese unit passing
through on its way to the Cu Chi District and its role
in the recent Met Offensive, and headed for the
nearest target. Which were PIZZA II's. Which was
us.

As Thuong, his men, and the Pizzas were moving towards Nui Nui Nui Nu?, I poured another round of Satchel Charges and Trung suddenly revealed yet another facet of his complex Asian self.

"Tien-Ti, I've been thinking about that duck, and about the prisoner you were telling me about, and about everything else we've been doing, and it seems to me that the perfect metaphor for God is a wrestling coach."

"Huh?," I responded.

"I've never told you that in my younger days I was a wrestler. In fact, I was pretty good. I finished first at the Bui Mui Dui District Championships in the 115-pound class, and I was second in the Province Championships. I could have placed at the nationals, but of course the war intervened. I loved wrestling almost as much as I love baseball."

"Huh?" I responded, aware once again that as soon as you think you know a Vietnamese, Something Happens to prove you wrong.

"Yes, wrestling is so symbolic, and you know how passionate we Vietnamese are about symbolism: the mat itself; the circle, that potent symbol of wholeness, circumscribing the area of competition; the two competitors, one in a light singlet, one in a dark, struggling apparently against each other but with the real struggle taking place within each individual, the lighter part of the soul struggling against the darker; the referee insuring that the struggle proceeds according to the rules; Heaven watching its offspring from its distance, knowing that the struggle often does not go according to the rules, but knowing also that it is in these moments when we must respond to the unexpected or the unfair that we achieve the greatest growth.

"I was very close to my coach. He was a very intelligent man who suffered much in life. He was a regimental commander in the war against the French—the French killed his wife and children in an air raid—when they bombed the wrong village by mistake, which of course turned out to be the right village—and when the VC formed the 9th Viet Cong Division he was made its commander. He was killed in the Tet Offensive.

"He prepared his wrestlers the best he could, and he was a master of wrestling technique and human psychology, but, as he would often say, it was not his role to Play the Game of Life for us. Once we were trained, and understood the rules and the karma of the sport, and the symbolism, then we had to proceed on our own. He would often say that even though he cared deeply about us, he could not keep us from the bumps and bruises of the sport, or of Life, and the two are the same, because of course wrestling is Life, and if he had been able to protect us he would not have, because it is the struggle itself which helps each of us to define our relationship to and with Heaven.

"I had to go out on the mat by myself, and I learned that he was correct: all of us—coach, wrestlers, referee were and are subject to the rules and the Will of Heaven, which are not always in accord, as you and I have learned so often in our time together."

Everyone has a breaking point, and suddenly, without a warning, I had gotten to mine.

So much had happened in the last year and soon-to-be-a-half: The So-Bo Theorem, booby-traps, hummingbirds, hummingbird farts, partying with the Viet Cong, killing the Viet Cong, waking up with a rat sleeping on my chest, being almost killed by the Viet Cong, sitting down to a rasher of rat, staring into the face of the prisoner with no face, the smell of decomposing bodies during breakfast, the terror of the Loon Foon Forrest, especially when the rat-fink Yang-Khi pinch hitter smashed that homer to tie the game in the ninth, the Met Offensive, the enemy being better supplied with our weapons than some of our guys were, the political corruption of our government, who cavalierly went to war with the Vietnamese without knowing anything about their culture, and who could have ended the war years ago by ordering the Dodgers back to Brooklyn, the political corruption of the government we were fighting to keep in power, the draft dodging I hadn't been smart enough to be able to do effectively, all of these things made sense, or at least some sort of sense, or at least some sort of Sicilian sense to the nephew of Rocco (the hairy-knuckled nogoodnik) Bovino, but no one, not a single person I had ever heard, or read, or read about, had ever said a single word about the Vietnamese engaging in high school wrestling.

What next, I thought to myself, What could possibly top sitting on the summit of Nui Nui Nui Nu? and discussing the Bui Mui Dui District finals with a Vietnamese sergeant with a penchant for philosophic introspection?

What could possibly top this? Would he next begin quoting from a Russian or a German philosopher? In the original, of course. Was there nothing about this beautiful, terrible, compelling country that was as it appeared to be?

"Du musst herrschen und gewinnen, Oder dienenund verlieren; Leiden oder triumpheren; Amboss oder Hammer sein," said Trung, in the midst of my reverie.

"What???????"

"That's from Goethe. My coach taught it to us. It means, 'You must either conquer and rule or lose and serve, suffer or triumph, and be the anvil or the hammer.' He also taught us the great philosopher Nguyen Van Han's famous response to Goethe's principle, 'Le hien phap, do douoc phuoc rhap, mai phien phuouc chrap.' (It is the Will of Heaven that each of us will conquer and lose, rule and serve, or how the fuck will anyone ever develop wisdom?)

Continued Trung, "So I see Heaven as a kind of cosmic wrestling coach, Who does care about us, even though it might be hard for you or I to see this now as we struggle on the mat; one Who is compelled by Its Own Logic to let the Game continue without interference, because how else will we gain the wisdom that will enable us to understand the Will of Heaven and someday aspire to Heaven?"

"Yeah," I said, "tell that to that poor kid with his face shot off. I'll bet he's ready to buy Nguyen Van Han's bullshit. Or tell that to you, when you were crying over that dead duck. Why were you questioning the Great Cosmic Wrestling Coach about the duck's Bad Break?"

"Bay was right," Trung replied, "you're so American. You have no Faith in Heaven."

"Au contraire," I replied, "I have great faith—in Satchel Charges," pouring another one, and you didn't answer the question about you and the duck."

"Ma~`ph^`~iy*a!!?~", Trung said, expressively (You and I and the thousands like us have to choose either wholeness or fragmentation, either love or the absence of love, which is evil, and if you accept evil you are doomed to become the worst parts of what we have seen and have done here, and it is sad beyond words that so many on both sides have died and have been maimed, but sadder still that so many have lost hope and faith, and to have lost hope and faith is to be alive on the outside but dead within, and if you accept wholeness, you must accept that there will be bad breaks, because

Heaven cannot and should not interfere with what
happens to us within the circle of Life, where each
of us has the opportunity to learn that the old truths
of love and honor and pride and compassion are not
clichés, but are rather the foundation stones of a
Life Well Lived, and it is true that the duckling had a
Bad Break, as did the soldier with no face, and I
cannot explain to you why it had to be so, any more
than I can explain to you why the horrible things that
we both have witnessed, and both have done, and
both have had done to us, had to happen, but I
know that despite these things we will endure, as
individual men and as a human race of men and
women, and not just endure, but evolve and
transcend, because you cannot ever forget that we
have also seen here courage and honor and hope
and compassion and pity and sacrifice and love,
from the men and women on both sides, and if it
was your Fate and the Fate of your fellow soldiers to
fight for a nation embodying the greatest principles
of humanity, in a war that represents the worst
impulses and darkest side of That Great Nation, and
then to be blamed for what you did and had to do by
those who sent you or by those who were silent
when you were sent, or by those who were just too
busy to notice, then that is just your Fate, and as is
always the case with Fate you must choose to
accept it and honor it and be honored by it, or you
can reject It, and whine and cry about the Great
Referee's bad call, but do not forget that always
throughout history someone had to take the road
less travelled, so that others could recognize the
True Road, and though this heavy burden was given
to you and your fellows, remember that Heaven

does not give to us a greater burden than we are able to carry, and, just as you must chose love or the absence of love, which is evil, and as you must make this choice now and on each day of the rest of your life, remember that I love you and you love me, and our love grew out of the same garden which grew the fate of the duckling and the soldier with no face, and all the rest of us. Do you understand this, my big-nosed friend, or are you truly as dumb as you look?)

"Xien le Viet, go pho tap lanh phai guop duop," I said, "hai phai tup chin vien thi lien pho dop xaun loc tinh mat phuoc ranh cam phang rang dai lient xi cho may phip, dap duop le omh lao diet," I paused, downing another large gulp of Satchel Charge, "phiet man hu rang slam bhang noc troup, chi cho chumg toi danh ban dia do o dau noi toi phu bhu zao lop diep miet anh cai loc dhop (Yes).

At that moment Corporal Quang stuck his head into the bunker and said, "Bhuddha, it stinks in here. Tien-Ti, you must have had hummingbirds again. Trung, how can you stand to be around him when he gets like this, especially in an enclosed space????? This has to be almost as bad as that PIZZA shit you guys were telling us about. Anyway, call the artillery and let's get the party started. We're ready to Get Down."

By the sheer accident that often influences human action, just as I was calling in a fake target that ostensibly had appeared on a McCarthy sensor, Thuong and his men were filing past the sensor in question, each man repeating to himself the mantra, "Greed is Good, and rampant and unfettered aggressive capitalism is empirical proof that Jesus H. Christ is the One True God, and Democracy is the best form of government, as long as the rich people get to make the important decisions and, most especially, get to be re-elected on a regular basis and therefore never have to work at a real job."

The McCarthy sensor, of course, noted nothing unorthodox in these thought patterns.

Truth to tell, even worry warts like me were not too worried about a serious VC attack. Even though Nui Nui Nui Nu? was out in the Middle of Nowhere, it was considered a safe haven by the Zebra Force. Surrounded on three sides by rice paddies and on the fourth by the Dong Ding River, it was impossible for the enemy to get to the hill without being seen during the day, and even at night any infantry assault would have to take place over open ground, into the teeth of the powerful artillery support that was available to the defenders, along with air support had the enemy made the attempt.

Commander Thuong's assault plan took into account the reality that it was impossible to fire a rocket that would land on the summit of Nui Nui Nui Nu?. Given the height differential between the jungle/rice paddy area and the top of Nui Nui Nui Nu?, the best launch angle a gunner could create would impact the rocket midway up the hill. But the deadly PIZZA II did not need anything like a direct hit to wreak its terrible Havoc. As the old Vietnamese saying goes, ""Phien le chrap, tien 'le stink'" (Shit might flow downhill, but really stinky smells, like articulate, well-dressed incompetents and politicians, tend to rise, and quickly.).

The Cong would launch the 3 PIZZA II's at Nui Nui Nui Nu?, and, as the overpowering stench was incapacitating the defenders (probably so quickly that the radio operator would be unable to send a call for Help), a squad of sappers would climb Nui Nui Nui Nu? and throw Satchel Charges (the ones that go Boom, not the potable kind) into the perimeter and then escape.

The first hint of trouble on the summit came when our lookout noticed the flash of the first PIZZA's firing. "Incoming!" he cried, but without real concern, since even if well aimed, the typical Soviet 122 MM rocket could cause no damage to anyone on the top of Nui Nui Nui Nu? But then, the PIZZA II was not a normal weapon.

The rocket hit a little higher than three quarters up the hill (the improved rocket design showing its worth) and immediately the horrible, disgusting, inhuman smell of fermented anchovy pizza paste began rolling up Nui Nui Nui Nu?. I had come out of the command bunker at the lookout's shout, and my keen nose was the first to recognize the True Danger: "Oh, God, that's a PIZZA." At the same instant the lookout shouted, "More incoming. I see two more flashes."

The dread cry "Incoming PIZZAs" filled the night. Trung responded brilliantly, as usual. He recognized the enemy strategy and knew that we would have to have protection when the massive stink of several PIZZAs reduced us to helpless, quivering, retching wrecks. He ran for the command bunker and began calling for all the artillery and air support he could get. Fortunately, Major Hyperbole's men had already begun to respond to our original, false indication of a target, so artillery fire began arriving seconds after the first PIZZA hit.

Our artillery fire, of course, was aimed at the coordinates of the McCarthy sensor, so the rounds needed to be adjusted, and quickly. Trung did this, feeding to the artillery spotter the approximate coordinates of the Cong firing position and then calling for more shells to fall along the approach route the sappers would have to take, Trung having immediately divined the enemy strategy. His experience during the aftermath of the assault on Camp Breast cut his reaction time to the minimum.

Almost instantaneously, 14 of the 15 Zebra Force members on Nui Nui Nui Nu? were in varying stages of Big Trouble, as the impossible-to-describe smell rolled over the top of the hill.

Trung, though shaken, was still able to function. Retching, reeling, he hung on and stayed at his post in the command bunker, orchestrating more artillery and then directing the fire of the first Snoopy that arrived within minutes (The Snoopy was a twin-engine C-47 fitted out with mini-guns, a sort of super-fast modern Gatling gun. The plane could, by virtue of its slow speed, circle a battlefield and pour down hundreds of thousands of rounds in minutes. Grunts gave the mini-gun-carrying C-47's the nickname of Snoopy because when the plane prepared to fire, the pilot raised one wing and lowered the other, much as a dog does when doing number one; when the guns fired, a rain of pee came down on the unfortunates who were the target. At night, when every fifth round from the mini-guns was a tracer round, the sight was both terrible and beautiful, depending on whether you were the target or were about to get overrun by the target.)

Thuong might have been in the grips of a nuop duop, but he didn't get to be a VC District Commander by being a Fool. And, as the prisoner we talked to later noted, "Getting a good blow job (Of course, it would take a philosopher of the brilliance of Hung Wai Lo ((a noted Vietnamese sexologist/Confuscanist of the sixteenth Century)) to imagine that state of consciousness known as 'a bad blow job') is difficult these days, what with the war and the constant presence of our Beloved (((Ptui!))) Comrades from the North, but even the great Hung Wai Lo would not be able to imagine how one could get a blow job when dead, so even though he was Royally Pissed at you Lo Muon Phfiets, he decided to follow Uncle Ho's rule of running away to Fight Another Day and, not coincidentally, be able to get a blow job another day."

When Captain Cohen heard that we were under attack by PIZZAs, he immediately got on a chopper and came to our rescue with a company of Screaming Hummingbirds, whom he stationed around the base of Nui Nui Nui Nu?

During our after-action debriefing, it was clear that two things had saved us: First, "Phien le chrap, tien 'le stink'" notwithstanding, the fact that the PIZZAs had not landed on the summit gave us a second or two more reaction time than we would otherwise have had (and also reduced the terrible impact of that disgusting smell on our psyches, or whatever was left of them by this time); and, second, we had Trung.

Trung himself gave a lot of the credit for our successful defense to me: "Listen, Dai Uy (Captain), I've been around Puggelli for over a year, and after thousands and thousands of his farts, my nose just isn't as susceptible to foul odors as it used to be. I mean, the PIZZAs affected me, but I could still function. You want to see what I mean by being desensitized, go down into the command bunker. It's been hours since his last hummingbird fart and the air still makes your eyes water."

Cohen put me in for a medal, which I got. Go Figure.

Part V: Our Hero comes home, but does not have an easy time of it.

Chapter 1
He Meets the Love of His Life, but Does Not Prosper

I met Donna LaMadonna at a party shortly after I had come home, "Gleebflob," I said when introduced to her. "Skeezel." I fell in love. She was the essence of "bui" ("bui" is a Vietnamese word with variant meanings, depending on syllabic emphasis and context: the first, the more traditional usage, is "young female person naked from the waist up who is wearing traditional black pajamas made of soft, clinging cotton."; the second meaning, which developed during the period of French and then American intervention, is "young female person naked from the waist up who is wearing skin-tight black leather pants with mid-thigh shiny black boots with spike heels and who is carrying a whip.")

Long story short, I thought I had gone from Hell to Heaven.

I wanted to marry Donna and have three fat bambinos, one of whom would grow up and wrestle for Iowa, one of whom would become an option quarterback for Oklahoma, and one of whom would become a principal dancer with the New York City Ballet. Naturally, I went to Uncle Rocco and asked him for his opinion of the proposed match.

"She won't let you watch the football games. You know it makes you crazy when women don't let you watch the football games."

Not to worry. DLM was even more a football fanatic than I. On our second date, over hot fudge sundaes, she advised me to bet on Oklahoma in the upcoming OU-Nebraska game, even though Nebraska was a 10-point favorite and playing at home. When I mentioned the point spread and home-field advantage, DLM, pausing to munch a cherry between her pearly white teeth, said that the OU guards and center would dominate the Nebraska inside defense, thereby opening up the dive part of the option and insuring that the OU wishbone backs would have a field day outside NU's contain men, who would have to pack in tight to help stop the dive.

Not only had I survived Viet Nam, I had found a woman who understood the option play.

I was excited, but not excited enough to ignore the wisdom of my favorite uncle, so I prepared a small ambush for my beloved: "Dearest one, you who are the ricotta cheese in my lasagna, the lemon peel in my espresso, the sweet cream in my cannoli, what say we go to the Brooklyn Academy of Music this Sunday and see their magnificent production of 'Waiting for Godot'?"

Responded my darling, "You drink too much wine last night? You want to sit for three hours and watch that stupid play, and, what's worse, listen to the people around us whisper about how brilliant it is, when they don't know any better than we do what's going on up there, because NOTHING is going on? Let's get this straight: You want to subject us to such torture when we could be cuddled together on the couch in front of your TV watching the Cowboys and the Giants and indulging in some hanky-panky at half-time? Sweet Sausage, are you fucking nuts?"

With one argument dismissed, Rocco marshaled others: "She's a liberated woman who won't take care of you the way we Sicilians need; and I bet she can't cook."

Could she cook! Her lasagna was so good I didn't know what I liked more, her or her lasagna.

Shifting gears in the true Sicilian manner, Rocco pressed on in BS: "Mafia," he said ("You're seeing with your dick, not your eyes. You think she's special now. After you get married she'll become a 'mustache Carola.' " ((a Sicilian slang term for a traditional Italian girl with heavy fuzz on her upper lip who bores her husband, who always said he wanted a traditional Italian girl but is bored to death now that he has one, to death.)).).

Donna was anything but a potential "mustache Carola." She was already accepted into the NYU MBA program and planned on going into the stock market "because that's where the quick big bucks are." Then, having built a nest egg, she planned on starting her own financial consulting business and working out of her office at home, "so I can take care of you and our bambinos." And she was "not into dull sex, so get used to a lot of experimentation."

"Persistence" was Rocco's middle name, and he didn't stop trying: "She's a schiksa." (i. e., not of our kind). This time Uncle Rocco had a point. The LaMadonnas came from Northern Sicily, and we were from Southern Sicily. This important difference caused hotheads in both families to be against our marriage, but cooler heads countered that if Richard Nixon could talk with the Godless Chinks, then the world was changing rapidly, and maybe such significant differences could be overcome.

So things were looking good. Good, that is, until That Fateful Night. But let me back up for a second.

I had never told the LaMadonnas that I had been to Viet Nam. I learned soon after I got back that it was gauche to have been in Viet Nam and that no self-respecting person with any sense of propriety would have been caught dead near that country. So I told the La Madonna family that I couldn't remember where I had been or what I had done for almost two years.

To the La Madonna's, such a statement from an adult male Sicilian nephew of Rocco ("the extremely nasty and generally ill-humored Hammer") Bovino merited neither the concern, nor the alarm, nor the covert whispering that forced many Nam vets to resort to cases of selective amnesia about their recent pasts.

So whenever I experienced one of the adjustment problems that stood between many other vets and a

Return to Normalcy— periods of inexplicable depression, heavy nighttime sweats, jumping at sudden noises and refusing to go out of the house from July 2nd to the 6th, a dislike of crowds, and when Donna persuaded me to take her to a restaurant ("I'll melt your whistle when we get home.") I sat with my back to the wall where I could see the door, and watched everyone very carefully; and I slept each night with the Bowie knife I had carried in Nam—all of my quirks and more constituted Business As Usual for the males and females of the LaMadonna family.

Well, almost. In a flash of the infamous LaMadonna temper, Donna said to me one night as we prepared for bed, "You bring that knife to bed one more time and you get no nookie for a month. I don't understand this thing you have with that knife. You need a security blanket? That I understand, but get an Uzi. Don't you know anything about firepower? Ever try re-loading a Bowie? Ever put it on full automatic? Ever lay down a base of suppressing fire with a fucking knife? What'reyou, a numbnuts?"

Ah, memories! you know, life is a lot like the jungle. Everyone realizes there are booby traps all over the place, but who ever really believes he's going to step on one?

That Night I was at Donna's watching the Monday night football game. Donna's mother and uncle were going out to dinner. They were almost out the door when Mother Margarita stopped and said, "By the way, can we bring you back something?"

Donna, normally so engrossed in the game you could drop a bomb and she wouldn't notice, uncharacteristically looked up and said, "Bring us back a large anchovy pizza."

ZAP!!!!

Screaming "Pizzas! Pizzas!! Incoming Pizzas!!, I dove from the couch and hit the ground, grabbing Donna on the way and pulling her down with me. She raised her head (No doubt to ask in the typical LaMadonna fashion, "What the fuck is going on?") and I grabbed her hair and slammed her back down to the ground. "Stay down," I screamed. "They're shooting live Pizzas out there."

I knew we had to react fast if this was a serious enemy ground probe, and it obviously was, since the VC were using Pizzas. If they had timed the assault the way they did at Camp Breast, the sappers were probably slipping under the last roll of wire just as the first Pizzas were coming in.

Damn! I was right! A sapper (Mussolini, the LaMadonna family feline) came running into the bunker. I jumped up and threw a grenade (Margarita's favorite hot-pink vase) at the sapper. Snarling unintelligible curses at me, the sapper beat an un-sapper-like retreat.

Diving back to the ground, I low-crawled to the bunker's entrance, past a pair of stunned rookies who must have been seeing their first action. Jumping up again, I pulled both of them down with me. Disentangling myself and still not hearing our machine guns (Had they been Pizza-ed already?) I slithered out into the compound and began yelling to the radio man, "Get counter-Pizza fire right away or we're in Shit City. Call air support, call the navy, call the Marines, call God, get help, or we'll all be Pizza-ed!!"

The LaMadonna family thought my behavior that night strange. Her uncle, Donna told me later, was particularly angry: "OK OK, I can see diving on the floor every once in a while, just for practice. I do it myself. It keeps the reflexes sharp, and in our business, you gotta be quick...you never know when somebody might try to re-negotiate a deal. Bouncing Donna off the floor— who am I to tell a man how to keep his woman in line? Throwing the vase at Mussolini? I never liked that fat fucking cat, and pardon me, Margaritissima, that vase was so ugly it made me want to puke. So maybe the man does have some taste, after all. But where does he get this 'Pizzas! Pizzas! Incoming Pizzas!'? We hadn't even ordered the damn pizzas yet!!!"

"Grandpa Luigi was right: You can't trust Southern Sicilians. They're all nuts, and this one is the biggest nut job of them all. I mean, this is the Twentieth Century: Who sleeps with a knife anymore? Why doesn't he get an Uzi like any sane man would? My niece will not marry that man; I don't care who his uncle is."

Not knowing what to say to Donna, I said nothing, which I now know was a mistake.

But at the time my top priority was getting a grip on myself. A long time had passed since the war, and suddenly, for no reason at all, I'm suddenly losing control. I hear or see the word "Pizza" and I'm back in Nam.

....I'm driving down Broadway with my cousin and his wife and we go past a Ray's Pizzas: ZONK I cut the ignition and roll out of the jeep into a slit trench, screaming "Pizzas! Pizzas! Incoming Pizzas!"

....I'm baby-sitting Tommy, my cousin's five-year-old kid, and we're watching Bert and Ernie argue about cookies when he gets bored (I wasn't bored. I love Bert and Ernie.) and grabs the remote and changes channels, right into a commercial for Gino's Pizzas. WHAP! I grab the messed-up medic (Tommy) and throw him into the bunker, and then go back and get the even more messed-up guy the medic was working on when he was messed up (Tommy's favorite teddy bear, Herman) and throw him into the bunker. Then I go looking for my rifle.

Tommy thought the whole thing was fun. My cousin and his wife, who didn't know I had been in Viet Nam—I told them I had been wandering in Europe with Sylvester Stallone, Seeking the Meaning of Life—attributed my behavior to a diet-caused hormone imbalance (being crazy because of a diet-caused hormone imbalance was the rage in Manhattan that year.).

As if having Viet Nam come unbidden out of my closet wasn't bad enough, Donna and I were having sexual problems. There were times, pardon my French, when I couldn't get it up, and if you couldn't get it up for Donna, then something was rotten in Brooklyn.

One night I said to Donna over a late supper (at my place, of course, as I was persona non-grata at the LaMadonna home),"Maybe I should get some professional help."

"Nonsense," said she, "occasional sexual dysfunction is common among men like you who worry a lot. More lasagna?"

"No, thanks, I said, "I'm not into lasagna lately."

Well, of course, that tossed the water buffalo shit into the rotor blade, as Sgt. Trung used to say. Somewhere there might be a confirmed, dedicated gay man who would not be aroused by the sight of a naked Donna, but no one in her young life had ever gone unaffected by a naked Donna lasagna.

"Fuck you," she screamed, throwing her napkin, knife, fork, plate, and glass at me, "you're getting help! This shit has gone far enough!"

Give me credit, when I need help, I go and get the best there is. Miriam was a liberal upper West Side woman who had taken a psychology course in college and who was dating and planning to marry a married psychologist from Woodmere, Long Island. Not content to rest upon as solid a set of psychological credentials as you could find in New

York, Miriam also watched soap operas and talked regularly with her hair stylist.

It turned out that Miriam's practice included a number of other Nam vets.

"You guys have a lot of the same problems," she told me after a session. "You all have negative attitudes. You took the things that happened in Viet Nam personally and now you're taking it personally that the country doesn't give a shit about either you or your service and is, in fact, holding that service against you. Lighten up: this isn't personal; it's business. A war was lost. Somebody has to be blamed. There is no free lunch."

"But how can I not take it personally?" I asked. "I was there, I am here. Of course I take it personally. I'm a person."

"Two," she ignored me, the sign of a truly competent professional in the field, "you're maladjusted. I want you to read James Baldwin's essay on creativity. He says that there are two kinds of people in the world, those who accept society's judgments unquestioningly and those who see that a lot of those judgments are wrong because they're based on premises that aren't real. This second category includes artists, women who have tried to convince employers that being a housewife is actually meaningful work, and veterans of lost wars. Baldwin says that people in this category ought to be rounded up, sent to Nome, Alaska, and put into concentration camps."

"That's not true," I said. "I read that essay. Baldwin says that society needs artists and other people who can see the difference between 'what's supposed to be' and 'what actually is', because without such people, how does 'what's supposed to be but isn't' ever get to be 'what's supposed to be and is'?"

"Who are you going to listen to," screamed Miriam, "your shrink or a fag schwartzer who hasn't made as much money in his life as I made last year? Besides, who's diving under a table every five minutes, me? No! You! You're sick. You're maladjusted, but don't worry. I'm here to help you."

With Miriam's help, I began to put my life back together again.

Meanwhile, the once-strong fortress of my relationship with Donna was being pounded by the artillery of circumstance: the moderates in the LaMadonna family had been overwhelmed. Donna's grandfather announced, "The marriage is off. Southern Sicilians don't play with a full deck."

The long hours I had to spend in therapy were also taking their toll, cutting, as they were, into time I used to spend with Donna. And then, when we were together, we talked about everything except what we needed to talk about.

Finally, I told her about the war.

She had a difficult time understanding. She knew
no other veterans: each of her four brothers had
been given a deferment because he was an orphan
and an only child who was the sole support of his
crippled parents; and all her male friends from
college had been granted deferments because they
were genuinely afraid of being blown to bits and
could either quote philosophers who agreed that
fear is scary or had letters from psychiatrists who
certified that this fear was genuine.

I tried to describe to Donna the bleak despair of
lying helplessly in your hole, hugging the ground in
a way you never held your mother, all the while
hoping and praying that the enemy was shooting
normal missiles full of explosives and razor-edged
steel, and not those horrible, terrifying Pizzas.

She said, "That's disgusting. No one should have to
do things like that. How could you put up with it?
How could you let people do that to you? How
could you do it to yourself? Why didn't you just
leave?"

I speak English, French, Russian, Vietnamese, and
Sicilian; I meet perfect strangers and we have
deeply personal discussions. But I didn't know what
to say, or how to say it, to the woman I loved.

As is often the case, the end came just when I
thought things were looking up.

With Miriam's help I was making great progress
towards becoming well adjusted. "Faggot, loser,

coward, person who clearly never went to Novenas," she would yell at me, "pervert, molester of young water buffaloes, mass murderer of innocent civilians, major deviation from the acceptable and/or accepted norm." On and on she would go, "fascist, drug addict, baby killer, forever warped and twisted personality, scum, moral cretin, person who would fart loudly in public places and not be ashamed," and I would not flinch. Then she would yell, "Pizzas, Pizzas, incoming Pizzas!!" and I'd flinch, but maintain control.

Then came the real test: "Great gobs of fermented anchovy pizza paste!!" That was tough, but after a lot of counseling and many Orthodox Thought meditation sessions, I could handle it.

Donna and I were getting along better, sort of, and the LaMadonna family was slowly beginning to unbend to me. Things looked like they might work out.

That Last Night, I was over at Donna's watching a "Rocky and Bullwinkle Retrospective." She was studying for two exams, one in her "Increasing Profitability Without Worrying Too Much About Increasing Productivity" course and one in "Leadership and Management of the Morons Who Inhabit the Contemporary Workforce" course.

Margarita had her bridge club over, and she asked me if I go out and pick up some pizzas.

"Sure," I said, sweating. "No sweat. How many do you want?"

"Get six," she said.

What kind?" I asked

"Two with mushroom, two with sausage, and two with anchovies. No, wait, make that two with extra anchovies. Tell Romeo to really pile on the anchovies. In fact, get all six with extra anchovies. Anchovies are the greatest. I just love anchovies, don't you?"

A year later Donna married a stock broker.

Chapter 2
Finally, Our Hero Finds a Niche, of Sorts

One day in May of 1979 I was walking down Columbus Avenue during an early heat wave, on my way to the gym. I had just passed 74th Street when I heard someone shout, "Incoming! Incoming!" I was flat on the pavement before my conscious mind realized that while there might be occasional combat on Columbus Avenue, especially during a clothing sale at one of the new upscale boutiques, it was unlikely that there would be incoming mortars or rockets (unless, of course someone was attempting to steal an apple from one of the many Korean fruit stores that had suddenly appeared on the Upper West Side, but few people, even Sicilians, were crazy enough to attempt to steal from a Korean). "Once an egg-sucking Yang Khi imperialist, always an egg-sucking Yang Khi imperialist, Tien Ti. How're they hanging, you minion of forces beyond your miserable ability to cope with?"

I couldn't recognize the speaker, and not simply because I was lying flat on the hot and dirty sidewalk. "Who is this asshole?" I thought. Clearly Asian and probably Vietnamese, he was dressed in an expensive three-piece suit, despite the heat, had a skewed sense of humor, and didn't know that one shouldn't end a clause with a preposition. And he knew my Vietnamese nickname.

"Don't you recognize me," he asked, making with the fingers of his right hand what appeared to be the "Hook 'em Horns" sign favored by fans of the University of Texas. "When in doubt, fake to the fullback and throw to the tight end," he said, grinning widely.

I got up, approached the speaker, and looked at him intently. Could it be????? It was!!!! Bay Vin, my old enemy/friend/fellow quaffer of rice wine and aficionado of the option play. "Phuoc, lem muot th hoang jai mien?" I said in my now rusty Vietnamese (Fuck, what dung heap have you been hiding under, you old VC pain in the ass, but isn't that a tautology?)

We immediately repaired to the nearest bar and got caught up on what had been happening in each other's lives.

Despite being on the winning side, Bay had not had a good time of it after the Communist victory. He had several strikes against him: one, he was a Southerner, and the North Vietnamese Powers That Be had never really trusted their Southern brethren, deeming them, with good reason, to be too laid back, too interested in partying, and too intellectually flexible; two, even by Southern standards, Bay was, as I had learned during the Great Bui Mui Dui District Get Down and Get Back Up Again Rice Wine Party and Cease Fire Bacchanal, somewhat of a Free Thinker, which made him by Northern standards, a heretic; three, his brusque style in the presence of colossal stupidity by his commanders had managed to piss off several important people in the VC leadership (Northerners, naturally), and now that the war was won, and they didn't need him anymore, the general attitude of these folk was "Phuoc Bay Vinh," which they did, thereby proving once again that no matter how great their differences, the Powers That Be are the same the whole world over.

Bay ended up in a "Re-orientation of the politically incorrect, conceptually questionable, and/or philosophically unsound" camp, where he spent four years clearing jungle to create more rice paddies, and then filling in the rice paddies to plant more jungle. "The experience gave me a sense of what it must have been like to be an American soldier in Viet Nam," he said. "No wonder you guys were as crazy as you were, or, in your case, are."

After being released from the camp, Bay decided that he had to get himself and his family out of Viet Nam and to, of all places, America, even though he would be going to a nation which had allowed the Dodgers to leave Brooklyn and go to, as he put it, "L fuckingptuii A."

To make a long story short, Bay and his family became boat people, survived a terrible time at sea, made it to a refugee camp, and, with the help of friends and foes who had already made it to America, including, he revealed, several ex-Zebra forcers and ex-Yangkhi Bashers, he and his wife, the delectable Hoa, his own two children, including Thang, whose life I had helped to save, and his

nephew Nguyen, the quick-footed young lad whom I
had met during the Cease Fire, made it to New York

They found a tiny apartment in Queens, opened up
a small family restaurant, plowed the profit back into
the business, opened up more restaurants, which
they staffed with fellow expatriates, discovered the
stock market "and the joys of investing in companies
that squeeze the worker unmercifully to generate
more corporate profit," and was now a rich capitalist
pig, and loving it.

 He was in Manhattan looking for a private high
school for his nephew, who was about to graduate
from Mary the Obsessive Virgin Middle School in
Astoria.

He knew that Trung had gotten out before the South
fell, largely thanks to the efforts of Captain Cohen,
who used his contacts in the military and in the state
department (the old Jewish Mafia again) to get
Trung out before the tanks rolled into Saigon. He
didn't know, of course, what had happened to his
best friend/worst enemy after 1975, and was
surprised to find out that Trung and I were living on
the same Upper West Side block, although the ex-
sergeant spent very little time home, having recently
met a high-profile model whose legs, Trung said,
were Heaven's way of answering the difficult
questions about Being and Essence which we had
raised during our rice-wine-quaffing days back in the
Nam.

When he arrived in New York in 1974, Trung took to the Big Apple the way, as Uncle Rocco puts it, "a Sicilian wife takes to snooping on her husband." Fluent in English, he got an equivalency diploma and then zoomed through Hunter college in three years and then entered NYU's MBA program, all the while working as a construction manager for Mike Brown, one of the top real estate developers in the City. Brown and Trung had met when they sat in adjoining seats at a Giants football game, and shared a passion for beer, football, and "chicks with long legs" (as Brown put it).

Trung had gone to work for Brown as a laborer and, with his formidable management skills and general intelligence, had immediately demonstrated his competence and Brown had promoted him quickly and often.

OK OK, I'll make this long story short. I know that you bought this book to read a serious and scholarly discussion about the true cause of the Viet Nam war, not a bunch of rambling anecdotes about friends and enemies and enemies who became friends.

Both Trung, Bay, and the other ex-Zebra Forcers and Yang Khi Bashers I would make or renew acquaintanceship with after this chance meeting agreed that while their spirits were rooted in Viet Nam, their hearts were at home in America, which continued to be a Beacon of Hope to those who were either wise enough or stupid enough, or both, to believe in a country that, while it produced

Thomas Jefferson, ESPN, Abraham Lincoln, college
football, and Martin Luther King, Jr., had still allowed
the Dodgers to move to L fuckingPtui A))).

At the time I ran into Trung I was teaching English
and history and coaching football and wrestling at
the McBurney School, located next to the West Side
YMCA on West 63rd Street.

Truth to tell, I was not a happy camper. Normally
disgruntled even in the best of times, periodically
affected by bouts of Gloom, Doom, and Depression,
I was not in Fine Fettle.   I had not yet gotten over
Donna. I was still angry at the treatment that
veterans had gotten when we returned from Viet
Nam to The World (especially from the people who
sent us to Viet Nam in the first place); and, of
course, I had never really gotten over Ebbetts Field
being turned into a housing project.

Uncle Rocco always says, "Don't get mad; get
even." I was determined to get mad AND get even.

And I would get even, I decided, by making sure
that more people like me and the other Least and
Dimmest citizens who had been sent to Viet Nam,
or who had been born there in the first place, would
get the benefit of the kind of education usually
reserved for the scions of the Best and Brightest.

Through Clever Political Maneuvering I became
McBurney's Director of Financial Aid (The guy who
had the job dropped dead of a heart attack and no
one else wanted the job.) and began to bring into

the school kids like the ones I grew up with and served with and fought against.

Most of the males I recruited ended up on the football and wrestling squads, which, of course, I coached, giving me additional chances to twist their impressionable young minds.

The first three of these, Mike Jones, a black from Harlem; Juan Martinez, a Puerto Rican from the Bronx; and Frank Falcone, an Italian kid from Queens, had just graduated (Each was the first in his family to graduate from high school) and all three would attend college in the fall, two at Ivy League schools. This year thirteen of my recruits would be scattered throughout the high school.

Bay's nephew Nguyen came to McBurney that fall and, getting bigger each year on an American diet combined with weight training, became an option quarterback. Bay finished his MBA and started several businesses on his own and with Peter Mancino, a real-estate friend of Mike Brown's.

Mancino, who, both Trung and I thought, bore a striking physical and metaphysical resemblance to Captain Cohen, was an honest real estate broker, a condition as much of an oxymoron in New York as is the concept of a straightforward Sicilian. Peter knew most of the important people in New York and had an in-depth understanding of the real estate business, but wasn't as good at the nuts and bolts of running a business.

His wife, Julie London, was not only a "xien thi luoup" (a woman of such surpassing intelligence, convivial personality, and staggering bui that you want to begin licking her feet while giving Thanks to Heaven that such beauty exists, and for a brief moment you suspend your belief that the people who run Heaven are about as Phuocked Up as the people who run This World).

London was also a Cua Phua Dua herself. After meeting Trung for the first time, London said to her husband, "That's the first guy you've thought about going into business with who could find his way out of a one-room house. You handle the outside shit and let Trung run the company and we'll make more money than even I can spend," which they did, and then Trung hired his cousin, Dzung, an ex-Yangkhi Basher, as his assistant at Western Consolidated Properties, and, with the extra time he had now, became my defensive backfield coach. (As further proof of London's Cua Phua Dua status, she said after she met me for the first time, "That man's psyche is even more crooked than his   nose.")

When Trung, Bay, and I dragged Captain Cohen out of retirement to be our line coach, we were ready to play Viet Cong football: Having little or none of what most teams took for granted—We had no home field, played all our games on the road, and had to practice in Central Park, amidst dog poop, the occasional gang fight, and sex perverts (including some who weren't on our football staff) —we relied upon truly sneaky and fiendishly clever tricks.

Bay and I combined the power of the I formation with the speed and flexibility of the option play and created the I-formation veer option offense. When he had the idea of using multiple formations combined with sending an offensive player in motion before the start of the play to further confuse the defense, the I Veer Option Motion Offense was born, which his nephew ran brilliantly for three years, and then his son ran even better for the next three.

Before the arrival of our coaching staff, McBurney's helmet logo had been a drawing of a guy playing a bagpipe. I had wanted to deep six the logo, but then Trung and Bay heard the mournful wail of a real bagpipe at the St. Patrick's Day Parade, an event and sound which, they agreed, captured the ambience of the Bui Mui Dui District Get Down Get Back Up Again Cease Fire and Rice Wine Bacchanal.

Even I had to admit that a well-played bagpipe produced just the kind of sweet and sour sound that appeals to the romantic core of a cynic, or to the cynical core of a romantic, or to the battered and beaten core of a Brooklyn Dodger fan.

So I knew that there was as much chance of getting rid of the bagpipe as there was of an American general choosing the Right Thing over That Which Advances his Career; or an American CEO choosing the Long Term Good over Short Term Profits. But the logo on our helmets now depicted Huyghen the Phuyghen, as drawn by Bay's still lovely wife, Hoa, as he spits a very large goober at The World in General, while playing a bagpipe.

We had a lot of laughs, won a lot of games (about Fucking Time we won something, Cohen or Trung or Bay or I would often say during a rice wine party after a game), had a lot of fun, and helped in the development of some fine young people.

Life, as May Thi Lin used to say, is like a water buffalo's shit: you never know what good will bloom out of a pile of really smelly crap. Nguyen, who turned out to have the same introspective streak as his uncle, became much more than just my option quarterback.

He had the habit of calling time out in critical situations, coming over to the sideline, and dropping into the discussion of the current tactical situation a Bay Vinh-like conundrum:

For example, against the undefeated Jericho Jayhawks, in the fourth quarter of the Long Island Conference championship game: "Tien-ti, mafiya mafiya. Mafiya?) (Honored Coach Big nose, we should run the outside veer to the tight end side because the corner will have to take the pitch man, our tight end will be able to seal the inside backer, the defensive end won't be able to cover both the dive back and me, and the safety won't be able to get there in time because he'll have to pre-rotate to the wide side and our twin receivers, and, by the way, is Emerson's conception of the Oversoul compatible with Jung's understanding of the collective unconscious, and if so, does this serendipity indicate a greater wholeness to the fabric of life than a disbelieving loner like you will ever admit?).

Or at a critical moment of a game against the hated Inquisitioners from St. Ignatius Loyola the Confirmed Casuist Regional Catholic High School, "Mafia, Tien Ti, phuop duoup xan han brung bung"): They're in an under-shifted split four defense and if we go Twins Right, Motion Left, 56 Sprint Draw, it's a guaranteed touchdown, Honored Coach Big Nose, and doesn't the very existence of this coaching staff and this team and this moment in time, and the good that you grievously injured souls are creating in the lives of us young people, despite your dirty language and even dirtier minds, or, perhaps, because of it and them, a good that is much like a small pebble dropped into the middle of the ponds of our Beings, setting off ripples that will continue to spread through us and through our children and throughout time and Eternity, don't these things indicate that there can be a redeeming quality to suffering that allows those of us who understand this and accept that which Heaven sends us, as difficult as it is to accept at times, to transcend the humanity into which we were born, to become greater than the sum of our parts, and to achieve a Oneness with Heaven, if only for a short time, a Oneness that constitutes at least an empirical confirmation of Heaven's existence?).

After Nguyen graduated, he went to Harvard, where he scored the winning touchdown against Yale in his senior year, got straight A's, and met someone named Gates, with whom he went into business. A few years later Nguyen had more money than his Esteemed Uncle, who by this time had more money than God.

Bay's son Thang went to Yale, where he scored the winning touchdown against Harvard his senior year, got straight A's, went to Med school, became an orthopedic surgeon, and, talk about luck, married a woman from New Rochelle who would give a Blow Job after marriage.

McBurney went out of business. Somewhere, Huyghen the Phuyghen is spitting a Very Large Goober at Wise Old Men who screw up A Good Thing.

Cohen had three children. They all play soccer, and one of them is an LA Dodger fan.

I began dating a shrink who thought I was either the craziest sane person she ever met or the sanest crazy person. Trung is convinced that she is right.

Trung married the model. Their daughter, Natasha, speaks fluent Vietnamese, English, and BS, and thinks that both I and my nose are cute. Go Figure.

The Dodgers still aren't in Brooklyn.

Life is like that.

Mafiya!!!!!

Hayden Brumbleloe

In August 1968 I was stationed at Fort Holabird in
Baltimore, Maryland, awaiting orders for Viet Nam.
One day I was assigned to accompany an officer to
clean out the off-post apartment of a soldier who
had just committed suicide.

During the ride from Fort Holabird to the apartment
located in a residential neighborhood in Baltimore,
the officer told me the few details that he knew
about the soldier who had killed himself: he was an
orphan, he had been to Viet Nam, had been sent to
Fort Holabird to finish the last five months of his
enlistment, and was scheduled to get out of the
Army on October 1.

To someone like me, who stood at the wrong end of
the Viet Nam pipeline and who had what seemed
like an eternity left to serve in the Army, the idea
that a man who had survived his tour, who had
come out of the good end of the pipeline, and who
was a few days from an Honorable Discharge and
freedom would kill himself was a concept as difficult
to understand as it would be to fathom the mind of
God.

In a desk in the apartment of the soldier who had
killed himself, Hayden Brumbeloe, I found a letter
written to himself, one page, single spaced.

I kept the letter and have it today. I have it next to
me as I write these words.

I kept the letter for two reasons: one, Hayden was
an orphan, and there was no immediate family

member to whom the letter would be given (his personal effects were being returned to the orphanage); two, I felt in a way that made no rational sense then, but which turned out to make a different kind of sense later, that he had written it to me.

After I had come back from Viet Nam I had a better sense of what Hayden wrote about in his letter.

Then and now, I wish that he hadn't killed himself, and would have loved to have had the chance to get to know him and to talk to him, both about what he had written in his letter and about what I had learned through my experiences.

In my time Over There I had come, not to an agreement with his action, not to an understanding of his action, but to a better understanding of the terrible, haunting forces that he brought home with him and that drove him to do what he did.

I had Hayden's letter on my desk when I wrote "God Bless America."

He has been with me, and in my heart, from that day to this.

The Russian Prisoner

Introduction

I tried for years to write about this incident.

There had been several credible reports in our area of Caucasians serving with VC units, and there were rumors that these Caucasians might be Russian advisors. When someone in the III Corps chain of prisoner custody said that a particular prisoner had said something in a language that sounded like Russian, alarms sounded all over the place, and the call went out for someone who spoke Russian. Unfortunately for me, Captain Jones, the commander of our sensor unit, remembered that I did.

It had turned out that Captain Jones and I were both fans of Russian literature, and in one of our conversations I had mentioned to him I had read several of the classics in the original; and that at the Induction Center at Fort Dix I had taken the Russian language test and scored highly enough to be classified as fluent for a non-native, a fluency that was the result of time spent with Dave, a Hungarian freedom-fighter and then refugee who taught me Russian when I worked for him in high school and after.

So a helicopter picked me up from Hill 507, where Bruce and I were monitoring a new kind of voice-activated sensor that we had dropped by helicopter in large numbers in a suspected VC base area. This particular sensor, equipped with a microphone, was designed to bury itself in the ground and, with plastic leaves extending from the top, look like a bush. Little did I know then that Hill 507 would, years later, become the site of the Battle of the Big Breasted Woman that is described in Darn Yangkhis.

The chopper dropped me off at the helipad of the Long Binh prison hospital so I could interrogate the Russian prisoner.

Who turned out to be a thoroughly Vietnamese VC who had been shot in the face and who had no jaw or tongue. And he was in better shape than most of the rest of the prisoners in the ward.

I got on the radio and told Captain Jones that the Russian prisoner was Vietnamese and he couldn't talk anyway because he had no jaw or tongue; and Captain Jones said, "You were sent up there to talk Russian to him, so talk Russian." And so I went back into the ward and asked him questions in Russian.

Communicating this story and its impact on me in traditional language required a writing talent far greater than mine, and my repeated attempts to Do the Impossible ended in the waste basket.

Then in 1982 a friend gave me a copy of Rollo May's "The Courage to Create," which I read in an afternoon. I liked his point that the act of creation requires a courage, first to intuit the proper path and then to follow it, no matter how unorthodox the path might be.

Two days later, as I was walking to the gym housed in the basement of the Parker Meridien Hotel in mid-town Manhattan, I saw in a blinding flash how to write the story. I went back to my apartment, sat down, and wrote what follows, did not change a word then, and have not changed a word since.

The Russian Prisoner

.... so then I go back into the ward where the prisoners are and I sit down on the empty bed next to the guy with no face who's leaning back against the wall with this swollen blob of bandage wound around his neck where his face used to be and from the bottom of the blob grows a drop of blood tiny first that gets big and fat drip pause dripping down the front of his shirt and he turns his head just a little which is about all he can do and his eyes look right at me and all of a sudden I know that he wants to ask me The Question which of course he can't do but I find myself saying to him don't even think about asking me because I have no idea what the answer is certainly no more than you and probably a lot less

and then in the middle of the ward a scream starts up and down and over and around and back it goes again this cry which doesn't sound like anything I've heard before but which for no good reason makes me think of the squealing of this woodchuck I shot when I was a kid and you could certainly see why this guy is hurting because his stomach is so swelled up that he looks like a woman ripe to pop an kid and I guess he was gutshot maybe with an M-16 round that was spinning when it hit him and God himself couldn't put humpty dumpty back together again after that

and just then I feel a hand on my shoulder and I look up and its another Vietnamese but this one was wounded a while ago and has recovered if you don't count the dent in his head where part of his brain used to be and drool bubbled and dribbled from the corner of his mouth spinning out in a long thin line that hung and bobbed and broke off and fell on his hand and on my shoulder and all the while drip pause drip pause drip and the scream goes up and down and over and around again and again even though it doesn't know where it's going to or even where it came from but it has to keep on going because just what else is there to do

and then three beds down the row somebody else begins to moan like a small sad wind going softly through the forest and this guy has both legs gone just above the knee it must have been not long ago and his thighs have swelled up like big fat sausages ready to burst in the frying pan

so I go out through the back of the ward and sit down next to a stiff on a stretcher and I guess I must have gone to sleep because the next thing I know I wake up next to the stiff who doesn't have a left arm but who does have a hole in his middle where his bellybutton used to be and then this big black spider climbs out of the hole in his middle and comes crawling after me so I get up and run I mean I never liked bugs even when I was a kid

and I run to my jeep and hop in but the damned bug crawls up the side of the jeep and sits itself in the other seat looking at me like it doesn't have a single good intention in the whole wide world and waving its arms or legs or whatever those things are and so naturally I jump out of the jeep and run down the street to the NCO club because I'm sure they don't let spiders into the NCO club and I sit at the bar and they got Star Trek on the Armed Forces Network TV and I'm sweating like I do in the jungle so I turn to ask the bartender why the air-conditioning isn't working and he says what?'reyoucrazy? it's freezing in here so I don't say anything else and turn back to watch Star Trek and I almost lose it then and there because and don't ask me how he did it that damn spider is right up there on the screen so I run out of the club

and of course the way my luck is running what do I see sitting in the middle of the street but the spider so I take off running fast and it takes off crawling fast and I run faster and it crawls faster and I run into the first building I come to and it turns out to be one of the American wards in the hospital and I know that this is not a real bright move even as I'm doing it because it's going to be scream moan scream drip pause drip bubble dribble drool all over again but take it from me being harassed by a big fat spider who just crawled out of some stiff's gut can make you do some strange things

and as soon as I heard the door close behind me I know that things have gone from bad to worse because for sure there are going to be more spiders in this place and I can't go back out the way I came in because there's a spider there and what in God's name am I going to do if I make it home and the damn spider crawls into the kitchen after me and climbs up on Mom's favorite table I can just see it Hi Mom I'm home and by the way here's the spider that 's going to follow me around for the rest of my

life what's that ? you can't see him?
what'reyou?crazy the damn bug is as plain as the
nose on your face and I take off running down the
aisle between the rows trying to get out of there and
I'm careful not to look to the right or left because I
don't right now want to see any other spiders come
crawling out of any other strange places

and right near the end of the aisle I stop wham like I
ran into a wall and I could see down this long tunnel
to the very end of it all to where It made sense but
of course exactly how it made sense was way
beyond me although I remember wishing I could tell
the guy with no face that there was an answer to his
question and

then some nurse came up to me and said
Areyouallright? and What'reyoudoinghere? and I
saidsomething and then I went outside and the
spider was gone Thank God and so I got into my
jeep and drove back to the firebase

where I got out a brand new bottle of Jack Daniels
and sat there on the mud floor of our bunker
drinking whiskey mixed with warmcherryKoolAid
from a canteencup crusted with little bits of crud and
Bruce said What'reyoucrazy?that's disgusting throw
that crap out and use coke we got cases of the stuff
but I said no what I want to do is to sit here and
drink Jack Daniels with warmcherryKoolAid and
that's what I'm going to do and that's what I did

God Bless America

Introduction

I wrote this in 1980, when America was in a mess much like today's mess, and not long after the Ray of Hope generated by the American hockey team's improbable run to the Olympic gold medal. I had been trying for years to write something that put into perspective my experiences in the war, the war itself, and the condition of our country.

I was especially interested in trying to put into words for a non-veteran reader a description of the Something that happens in war, a Something that can, unless one is careful, transform the heart into a stone; a Something which, even if one *is* careful, you must deal with and take control of if you are ever to fully return home.

I hoped that in the process of so doing I would find the language that would help me understand what had happened to me.

In multiple attempts over multiple years I had failed miserably to write what I was trying to write. Then one day, after seeing a commercial for Contac cold capsules, which were small capsules full of little tiny time pills, I got the idea for the opening line and for the piece's metaphor; and then the piece flowed out.

God Bless America
A Different Kind of Love Story

Viet Nam was a contact capsule. A day will be winding along its normal route and...POP!...there goes yet another little tiny time pill and there goes that certain part of your brain careening out of control while the straight part tries to put things back together before someone notices that something is out of whack.

Each veteran adapts to this condition in his own way. I have gotten so good that I now manage with a degree of ease. Teaching a class, coaching a game—I seem quite normal when a little tiny time pill goes off, much like my alcoholic Uncle John, who can be soused to the gills and yet do his job with perfect aplomb.

Take the other day as an example. I was in the trainer's room taping a wrestler's injured ankle. One of the other coaches asked me if I had seen "The Deer Hunter" or "Apocalypse Now" on HBO. I replied that I hadn't. He said that I probably shouldn't, as the films might cause nightmares. I laughed. "With all the pretty women in this world," I responded, "you think I'm going to waste my dreams on Viet Nam? I dream about..."—and...POP!...for no good reason at all I was thinking of Kevin.

Kevin and I had been through basic training together. Sent to Nam at the same time, we met by chance one day while we were both visiting the 101st Division base camp. We decided to stay there for the night so we could drink some beer and reminisce.

Kevin was a medic with the First Air Calvary Division. He had just returned from a trip to the boonies (the jungle) during which his unit had been suddenly and savagely mauled.

The first person Kevin had tried to save that night died in his arms while calling for a mother who was a half a world away. And then things got worse. We talked about the incident briefly. But what could you *really* say? After much beer and a little reminiscing, we went to sleep.

Suddenly I sat straight up, stunningly catapulted into consciousness by something I could not name. Then I understood: Kevin was screaming. The sound was full and long and high and absolutely unwavering. If a watch could speak, and you wound its mainspring so tightly that it could stand no more and burst, the watch would make a sound like Kevin's.

I don't know how long the moment lasted. It was one of those instants—Nam was a Pandora's Box full of them—that made complete mockery of the stern and unbending logic of seconds and minutes. When he was done giving himself to the night, Kevin collapsed back on his bunk.

I never asked him what happened. We were tough then: one solved his own problems.

But then again, maybe one didn't. A good friend of mine is in the anomalous position of being a lawyer and a combat veteran of Nam. (Most of the professions understandably have few Viet Nam veterans. After all, murdering fascist baby-killing drug addicts *are* a trifle unstable.)

David works for a top firm in New York. Smart and tough, he is an excellent lawyer with a great future. (as long, he says, as he keeps quiet about what he is.)

One day David is scheduled to interview a candidate for a position in his firm. The candidate's resume reads like a champion's pedigree: Choate, Yale, Harvard Law, and an initial practice with a prestigious Boston firm. If you cut his name, it would bleed blue all over its Roman numeral. The guy walks into Dave's office and says "Hello" in a voice dripping with certainty. After all, in his world, righteousness is inevitably rewarded. From another world, Dave sits there and…POP!...

My friend, who has never this happen to him in all the years since Nam, begins questioning the kid, at first half in jest and only half seriously.

David: *I see by your resume you were never in the service, although it appears as though you were eligible. What happened?*

Candidate: *I don't follow the question. What do you mean, 'What happened?'*

David: *How did you beat the draft?*

Candidate: *(a bit offended at David's crude language) My father is a friend of Senator *** They arranged something.*

And suddenly for David it's not half in jest anymore. He continues:

David: *How can a lawyer justify the use of special influence?*

What about the person who had to go in your place? Was what you arranged fair to him?

A good lawyer must have as fine a moral sense as a good doctor. Was this action characteristic of your moral sense?

The Candidate sits there, confused. This is an interview for a legal position. What is the problem with his guy? What kinds of questions are these?

David knows he has to cut himself off and he does. He didn't become a successful Big Apple lawyer by losing control. But before he became a successful Big Apple lawyer, he spent three days on Hamburger Hill.[2]And sometimes you can't help it, those damn little tiny time pills have a mind of their own.

David finishes the interview, calls me up, and we have lunch. As we walk back to his office, he stops, rests his hand on a parking meter, and stares off into the crowded canyons of Manhattan. Perhaps

---

[2] In a war that made little sense, Hamburger Hill was an event that still managed to shock with its utter senselessness. Fought in 1969 in a rugged, desolate region, miles from any civilian population, the battle developed on one of the many nameless hills that covered the area. While U.S. generals defended the operation as a tactical necessity designed to disrupt enemy supply lines, most American soldiers believed that its real purpose was to produce the high enemy body count the American government so often used to document the success of its military strategy. Almost 500 Americans were Killed In Action in the three days of appallingly vicious fighting that gave the Hill its name. According to survivors who fought there, the actual toll was much higher. Shortly after American troops captured the summit of Hamburger Hill, the U.S. high command withdrew them, leaving the bleak and bloody ground as a mute testament to the monumental human sacrifice that these men had poured out upon it.

he is remembering that long, long walk up Hamburger Hill, with trouble patiently waiting at the top and with fear and hope and time all rushing together in an accelerating avalanche of anticipation until at last the North Vietnamese opened up. Perhaps he is not thinking about the North Vietnamese at all. He begins crying and pounding his fist on the meter and saying over and over, "I hate the rotten bastards. God, I hate the rotten bastards."

Unlike David, I spend a good deal of time in conscious thought about Viet Nam. I do so because I am a closet schizophrenic. Fred, the name of my other self, is the solid and upstanding citizen I would have become if I hadn't become a worthless hippy freak.

I'm actually quite proud of Fred, although I wouldn't reveal such a sentiment to him. He makes good money, reads New York Magazine, goes to church and has a family. However, my relationship with Fred can best be described as a state of deteriorating détente. He bothers me constantly and we argue interminably, especially about life, America, and Viet Nam (Fred didn't go, what with college and grad school …)

The other day, for example, Fred was berating me because of my admittedly irrational but nonetheless violent dislike for former Iranian hostage Barry Rosen. "Leave the poor guy alone," said Fred. "So what if he's being treated like a hero. He is a hero."

"But…" I began.

"Shut up," snapped Fred, "and listen. Bitch, bitch, bitch, that's all you ever do. You veterans always separate the country into two parts, 'we veterans' and 'you others.' What in hell is your problem anyway? All of us are Americans, aren't we? That stupid war has been over for years. Forget it and grow up."

Why the dichotomy "we" and "you" when, as Fred correctly indicates, we are both parts of the same whole? Because a split is there, a San Andreas fault running through this country's societal personality, a condition unique in American history.

Perhaps this aberration exists because Viet Nam was a blow that fractured lives along class lines. I certainly don't mean this statement in any orthodox sense. The parameters of the classes, while partly economic, were by no means completely so.

Yet it remains a fact that a massive cultural experience developed in this country and overwhelming percentages of select groups of Americans were able first to reject its existence and then to ignore its significance and consequences.

If Fred were here (he's at a business conference), he would jump in and say, "Numbers, damn it! Give me statistics that document what you say. Glittering generalities, outlandish hyperboles, that's all you people ever use."

But I will not document my statement with specific statistics. Veterans have an inherent mistrust of specific statistical examples.

I stepped on a booby trap thirty-five yards from a village listed in the "Completely Secure" category on the American High Command's impressive statistics board in Saigon. At the time 95.2% of all villages in Viet Nam were classified as

"Completely Secure" or "Secure." After all they had to be if we were winning the war, and we had to be winning the war because our government said we were. Three days later a good friend of mine was killed in another "Completely Secure" village.

And the beat goes on: a few weeks ago I heard a government spokesman announce in conjunction with a labor dispute that if you looked at the figures properly, three times ten did not exceed twenty-one. (I must apologize for my irreverence toward The Powers That Be. "What are you," Fred always says, "a fucking pinko?")

As the supportive evidence for my outlandish exaggerations, I will introduce only the unscientific "boonie barometer," a homespun evaluative mechanism that was popular in Viet Nam's rice paddies and bunkers. Those utilizing the boonie barometer first carefully considered the words, facts, and figures that experts would marshal to explain this particular war. Then they discarded them all in favor of the two blunt conclusions that coincided with reality was we lived it: where bullets were flying, there you would find high concentrations of minorities and low-rent whites; where bullets were not flying, there you would find everyone else.

Our opponents were not nice people, but they did a better job at making that war what war should be, a burden shouldered by the entire communal family. I don't claim that the North Vietnamese and Viet Cong fighting force completely mirrored all levels of the society that bore it. But they tried, all of our propaganda to the contrary, and they succeeded to the limited degree that God grants human success.

Their effort and achievement explained why, year after year, as Time Magazine swayed one way, then another; as Westmoreland went and Abrams came; as Congress debated legality, morality, and practicality; the guys in the boonies bitched at the Cong with reluctant admiration and knew –I mean **knew**—we didn't have a prayer in hell of winning that war. And—it galled us bitterly—we didn't deserve to win it. They were doing it the right way and we were not.

And the beat goes on again. If you have any confidence in the new volunteer army: don't. Most of America isn't in this one either.

Fred, back from his conference, can't accept such "inflamed and irresponsible rhetoric" without a response. Says he, "Who the hell put you on the stage? You catch one bad break and complain the next twenty years. I have a family. I have a job. I don't bring the family to work and I don't bring the job home. All you guys have a martyr complex. Why did you have to bring that stupid war home anyway?"

Is it possible not to bring a war home? While in Viet Nam I spoke with North Vietnamese prisoners and defectors. Since then I have conversed with Israeli combat vets and American veterans of World War II and Korea. We are different in so many ways, but we are all alike in one way: each of us his own Snowden.

Snowden is a character from the pivotal scene in Joseph Heller's novel Catch-22. During a bombing mission, Yossarian, the hero, must give aid to the recently wounded Snowden. Yossarian knows that he faces a critical situation, but he has been well trained and should be able to manage. He bandages all the wounds he can find. As he works, he half-consciously congratulates himself that he has faced one of war's worst moments and he is, nevertheless, still coping.

But the gods of War are toying with Yossarian. Snowden's visible wounds are minor compared to the internal havoc that has been wrought: a fragment of a shell has pierced Snowden's side, passed through his body, and exited through the other side, effectively disemboweling him. Yossarian notices a spot of blood near Snowden's armpit and adjusts the flier's flak-suit, a device designed to protect the heart and other vital organs. As Yossarian adjusts the flak suit, Snowden's intestines spill out.

In a blinding instant, Yossarian understands the secret of war: whatever the preparation for it, no one can really cope. Function, perhaps, yes, but cope? No.

It is curious it had to be Heller, a former airman, who best described the disruptive thrust of an experience that is rarely a part of the impersonal air war and rarely absent from land combat. When you know Snowden, you know War. But such intimacy comes at a price, a price that makes it very difficult to come home again.

The trauma of Snowden is not primarily physical. While the terrible hurts caused by modern weaponry do befuddle the imagination, emergency rooms or random accidents can produce impressions of comparable magnitude. The hammering significance of Snowden is that this thing that has been done to a fellow human being, this savaging of the body that is the temple of the spirit, is not an accident, not a fluke, but the direct, purposeful consequence of war.

For men engaged in war the moment of knowing Snowden is not unlike the feeling of invasion and loss reported by women who have been raped. People can tell you it wasn't "your fault," you can know it wasn't "your fault," but a sense of deprivation remains and one feels soiled.

The sense of deprivation is real, because something has been stripped away: some of the moral and spiritual covering that surrounds each person's soul is no longer present. Like the protective enamel covering a tooth, one only notices it when it is not there.

Historically, the rape victim and the soldier returning home are wrapped in and reinforced by the collective spiritual values of family, friends, and society. But, as some women say and as an Israeli tankman told me late one night, even then the process of re-entry into normality is difficult. Even then, as a Marine Corps veteran of Iwo Jima confessed to me after countless beers, you have to live with your personal Snowden lurking in the back of your mind, devilishly darting into your awareness every five or seven years, or six minutes.

Yet, as both of these men explained in their different ways, you can coexist with Snowden because those close to you provide care and concern. True, no one fully understands, but they all try, and they all somehow share the right and wrong of the experience.

Except when Johnny came flying home from Viet Nam and tried to pick up the pieces of his life. America pretended that he didn't exist.

Perhaps it is this absence of concern that explains why, when Nam veterans mutter inarticulately into cameras and microphones, "We got screwed," they are not as inarticulate as they seem. War is a rampant invasion of one's secret parts. All soldiers get screwed.

But when a country refuses to come to terms with its war, when there is no reunion between the nation that accepted the war and the men who agreed to fight it, when there is no communal expiation of guilt and sorrow, then the screwing just goes on and on.

And, as with rape, one would need the wisdom of Solomon to judge who is the greater victim, the one who must accept the perversion of a love act or the one who was driven to initiate it.

The analogy with rape is, of course, imperfect. A country decides to go to war. Its citizens acquiesce in the decision, whether they care to admit it or not. Women do not choose to be raped. Yet many Nam veterans share an almost unknowing empathy with those women who have been raped and who must face the silent, looming conspiracy of thought that too often awaits them when they try to return home—after all, *it was your fault; after all, it didn't happen to me.*

This value stripping without any concurrent value reinforcement represents one of Viet Nam's most pernicious legacies. Like the war itself, this phenomenon has affected all Americans. If Viet

Nam veterans must grope their way back to stability without any real help, then what conclusion must be drawn about the nation that raised them and sent them? Perhaps there was no help given because no one had any to give.

If such a conclusion is accurate—and there is considerable evidence that it is—then not all of the war's casualties were injured in the combat zone. Can a nation's sense of itself suffer multiple fragment wounds? Perhaps so, because in this tense and gloomy country our injured self-image is making us very strange: barren, bottomline materialism stalks the streets, the young listen to lyrics like "all we are is dust in the wind," and too many people snort, drink, smoke, and inject themselves into a state of forgetfulness.

Dust we might be, but more than dust we have been. We forget our own heritage. To paraphrase the line from *Cool Hand Luke*, "What we have here is a failure to *understand*."

For while we see accurately, most clearly we do not understand. We Americans are better than our own view of ourselves.

The fire that has powered the engine of America has always burned partly on coal, but mostly on dreams. And the dreams haven't just been of another car or of a new coat, as some of us have attempted, rather successfully, to convince the rest of us. A large chunk of this country's coal has been composed of the American Dream of truth and freedom and right and goodness and helping others.

It is a sign of these disturbing times that few Americans would give voice to these private thoughts that many of us have, and it would be a rare politician who could utter them without provoking a rage of ridicule.

But the evidence denying the moral bankruptcy of this nation is incontrovertible: if there were nothing more to America than money, cars, and cocaine, why would so many people feel such a sense of loss?

But Fred, who knows you can't deposit dreams into a checking account, has an answer to such introspection. "Enough of the heart and flowers. Next you'll bring out a violin. Everybody has problems, but you assume that yours are the same as the country's. Stop with the analysis and go out and do something practical. You guys spend more time philosophizing than a Park Avenue shrink."

While Fred has a point, he is not completely correct: few veterans devote much time to philosophizing. We have our daily bread to earn. In fact, it is the earning of the daily bread that says much about us and the lingering influence of the war.

No factor better reflects the change that has come over America in recent generations than the absence of Viet Nam veterans from three areas of activity where one could reasonably expect to find them in some numbers, and where one could have found their predecessors after World War II: in college, teaching in high school, and in politics.

Where are we? Why are we not in college? Grasping for education? Why are we not in high school, teaching American history? Why are we not in politics, giving America the wisdom we gained through sweat and blood?

There are answers that, while true, are yet not the truth: the G.I. bill benefits aren't sufficient, teaching jobs are hard to find, you need connections to get into politics. The real answer is that we veterans cannot escape who we are.

What we are, first and foremost, is American, and to be American in this day and time is to be frustrated by a lack of faith.

Yes, we lost our faith somewhere in the swamps and jungles and then came home to find it had disappeared from America's towns and cities. Perhaps we didn't understand what was happening to us then, but we see it now.

Yet what we still don't see—and America can't come home from Viet Nam until we all see it— is that the faith we lost was an ephemeral belief grounded in the wrong source. It was a faith that others would define and create the American Dream *for us*, that someone would answer questions and solve problems *for us*.

What we had done was the most un-American thing of all: we had assigned responsibility for the American Dream to the faceless shadows who lurk behind that maliciously indefinite pronoun *they*.

So we—not *they*—made a mistake. But we will quadruple this mistake if we forget an essential point: the fact that we were wrong in our faith doesn't mean that this quality doesn't exist. The fact that we mourn its absence proves that it does.

Each of us must rekindle a faith in himself because, as we learned in the iron school of combat, a man must sometimes *be* an island unto himself; and we must all reclaim a belief in America because, as we learned when the combat was over, a man cannot *live* as an island unto himself.

And, although he would be the last to admit it, Fred wants to recapture his faith also. He's not the hardass he makes himself out to be. Fred will call us "suckers" and "dummies" for believing our government and for getting caught in the web of that war, but he cried when the American hockey team upset the Russian in the Olympics (he doesn't know I saw him, but I did).

A quick note before Fred comes back from the store (he always finds something to do when he knows I'm right): my more thoughtful non-veteran friends have often asked me about the conclusion of "The Deer Hunter," the singing of "God Bless America."

"Are veterans fools? Don't they appreciate the scene's consummate irony? Is it perhaps that they somehow see beyond the simple complexity of irony to a subtle wisdom that is hidden from those who have not been *out there*?"

I have no answer. We do love America and America is good. I knew this beyond question one day when I was 11,000 miles from home—tired, filthy, and miserable, with a loneliness that shriveled the heart—and I saw a tank roll by with a tiny American flag on it. I knew something then that I never truly comprehended as a child who watched the parades and listened to the speeches.

And so, although I don't like to stand up for National Anthem, I'll get up and sing "God Bless America."

And...
...POP!...

Fragments

Mom

When I was in grammar school at the Immaculate
Conception school in Amenia, New York, a common
play-yard insult was, "Your mother wore combat
boots." I was smart enough to know by the tone of
the comment that this was an insult when it was first
levelled at me, but I remember thinking, "Of course
she wore combat boots. Didn't everyone's mother
wear combat boots?"

My mother served in World War II, in the Women's
Army Corps. And she served overseas, in New
Guinea. As a young child is wont to do, I assumed
that my mother was normal and that her
experiences were normal. They weren't and she
wasn't.

When I knew that I was about to be drafted, and I
had to decide what I would do at this life-defining
fork in the road, she did not intrude herself into the
process of my decision, even though I was then an
only child, after the recent long and painful death of
my younger brother from cancer, and my going into
the military could conceivably result in the loss of
her now only child.

Her advice was, "You have to do what you think is
the right thing to do, and you will have to live with
the choice for the rest of your life, so think it through
and listen to yourself."

I did not realize at the time what integrity and love it took for her to do the thing that was the right thing for me and to guide me to walk on my path; I did not realize what integrity and love it took to not counsel me to walk on the path that would have been better and safer for her.

The Rat on my Chest

One night at Fire Support Base Concord, after my last shift of monitoring the sensor locations and calling in Fire Missions on suspected targets, I went to sleep on the top of the bunker in which we had our sensor monitoring equipment and radio.

When I woke up, I was looking into the face of a large rat who had been sleeping on my chest. The rat didn't blink; nor did I. We were both veterans.

He got up, ambled to a corner of the bunker, jumped to the ground, and disappeared into the detritus of the Fire Base. I got up, collected my things, and got into the relief truck that would take up back to Base Camp for breakfast.

The Most Memorable Bowel Movement I've Ever Had

One day I went to the Headquarters of the South Vietnamese Army's 21st Division to have lunch with a sergeant I had met at Fort Bliss while we were in the 12- week Vietnamese language course. He was the senior NCO adviser to the 21st Division Commander (a commander who would go on to become in Darn Yangkhis the officer who gives me the first inkling that the So-Bo Theorem is real).

After lunch I was preparing to catch a ride back to my unit when a familiar tightening of the bowels informed me that a trip to the latrine was necessary.

I was in the middle of a full Vietnamese Division and assorted other specialty units, so the usual American latrine hooch was not available. I asked a Vietnamese soldier, "Where is the latrine?" (The Vietnamese for this, "Cau tieu uh dau?", was simple enough that even I couldn't screw it up.)

He said, "Around the corner," and I replied, "Thank you," and followed his direction.

The latrine turned out to be a deep pit dug into the ground and crisscrossed by wooden planks. I suddenly realized that I would have to poop the way the Vietnamese soldiers did, by walking out on the planks, squatting, and doing my business. And if I slipped, I would fall into a pit of shit, and this time the shit was literal, not figurative.

Now Vietnamese are masters of squatting, and are also quite graceful and fluid in their movements, so for them the plank-walk out to the middle of the pit, the squat on narrow planks, the dump, and then the plank-walk back to safety was No Big Deal; for me it was a Very Big Deal.

And, of course, life being what it is, it just so happened that a platoon of ARVN airborne soldiers was lounging in the area and had noticed the American who had to shit in a Vietnamese latrine.

That day taught me that, while the fear of embarrassment is different from the fear of death or mutilation, it's not THAT different. There were several times in Viet Nam that I suspended my agnostic approach to Life and prayed with all my heart to God. This was one of them.

And so, remembering my Catholic school days and praying to God the Father; God the Son; and God the Holy Spirit; and a few other deities just in case; I did my business and made it back safely to the edge of the pit.

Joseph M. Puggelli

Made in the USA
Middletown, DE
11 February 2021

33526649R00139